First published in the United Kingdom in 1992
Cumbria Archive Service

© Cumbria County Council 1992

ISBN 0 9500371 4 1

This volume has been published with financial support
from
The Ellen Rose Fieldhouse Fund

Produced by Alan Sutton Publishing, Stroud, Glos.
Printed in Great Britain by The Bath Press, Avon

Cumbria A

TI
ELLEN ROSE
COLLEC

A catalogue of the papers and local
late Mrs. Ellen Rose Fieldhouse of I
and deposited at Cumbria Record C
extracts and photo

Contents

List of Plates

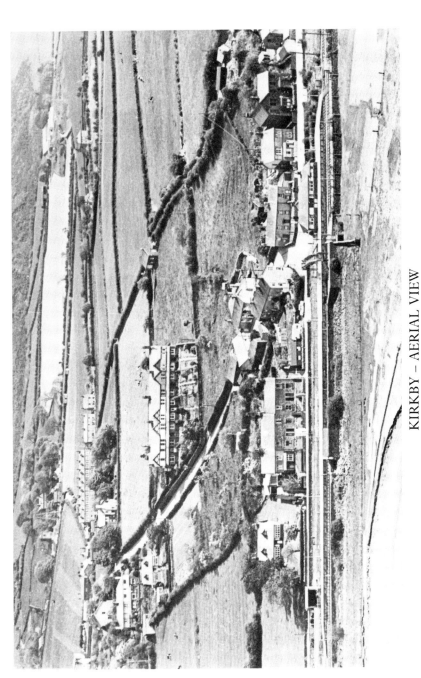

KIRKBY – AERIAL VIEW

A view of Kirkby Station and Sandside with the parish church and the Co-op built Herschell Terrace in the background.

(Photograph: courtesy of North West Evening Mail)

Ellen Rose Fieldhouse and Arthur Fieldhouse with Peter, 1934.

Preface

The Ellen Rose Fieldhouse Collection was deposited at the Cumbria Record Office, Barrow in October 1979. Mrs. Fieldhouse, who died in March 1983, lived for many years at Kirkby-in-Furness, Cumbria, and much of her collection relates to that village and to the surrounding area. Part of the collection was placed on exhibition in the Furness Museum at Barrow in January 1982.

Ellen Rose came to Barrow from Yorkshire in 1905 aged three years. Her father had served in the Scots Guards during the Boer War, and upon discharge took his family to Barrow-in-Furness as he considered it a town of great opportunity.

She remembered her childhood before the First World War with affection. Starting her education at St. George's Infant School, she was a bright and intelligent pupil who eventually entered college in 1920 and qualified as a teacher. Memories of her youth included walking around Barrow with her sisters, and travelling on the steamers 'Lady Evelyn' and 'Lady Moira' to Fleetwood. Ellen was on the last voyage of the old 'Philomel' and remembered taking a tram to Blackpool.

Her father was posted to France during the First World War and thus her childhood ended as greater responsibilities were thrust upon her.

After the war and after college, Ellen Rose taught for a while in Rotherham. Then, returning to Barrow, she helped in 1929 to reform the local branch of the Workers Education Association. The treasurer of the branch, Arthur Fieldhouse, took great interest in her progress and they were married in 1933. Their first home was a rented cottage in Soutergate. They later moved briefly to Walney Island, but soon returned to Kirkby to live at Seatle, Sandside.

In Kirkby, Ellen initially concentrated on domestic matters and took little part in village life. But soon a natural curiosity about the local dialect led her to a lifetime of interest and study of the locality. Arthur and Ellen Fieldhouse only left Kirkby in 1981, to live in the South of England. The legacy of these years of interest remains in the form of 'The Ellen Rose Fieldhouse Collection'.

The collection is the result of many years work in collecting booklets, magazine articles and copies of documents relating to the Kirkby area. The core of the collection comprises a total of 29 newscutting books and scrapbooks. There are also many photocopies of historical documents, together with research notes, exhibition captions, printed pamphlets, local and foreign illustrations, some primary archival sources and various artifacts. A few reels of recorded tape are included, with accompanying scripts, which reflect Mrs. Fieldhouse's interest in local dialect. There is also a small amount of more personal correspondence, photographs and material from Mrs. Fieldhouse's friends in America and elsewhere. The collection totals several thousand items in twelve boxes.

In the course of her research, Ellen assisted Lewis Kirby, an American who was tracing his family origins in England. In order to ensure its survival, she firstly offered her collection to Mr. Kirby. However at his suggestion, she ultimately gave it to his youngest son, Roger Hillersdon Wigg Kirby. Mr. Kirby was to serve as trustee until Roger came of age. The collection was made more widely available by being placed on indefinite loan at the Cumbria Record Office, Barrow.

Items from the collection can normally be consulted at the Record Office; details of opening hours etc. will be supplied on request. In accordance with common Record Office practice, access to a small amount of the more personal material will usually remain closed for up to 50 years from its date of origin.

This volume is almost entirely based on the work of Miss D.J.M. Rose, who listed the collection for the Cumbria Archives Department in 1980–81. Her work was made possible by financial assistance from an overseas foundation.

Cumbria Record Office,
140 Duke Street,
Barrow-in-Furness,
LA14 1XW

April 1992.

Abbreviation
(ph.) photostat copy

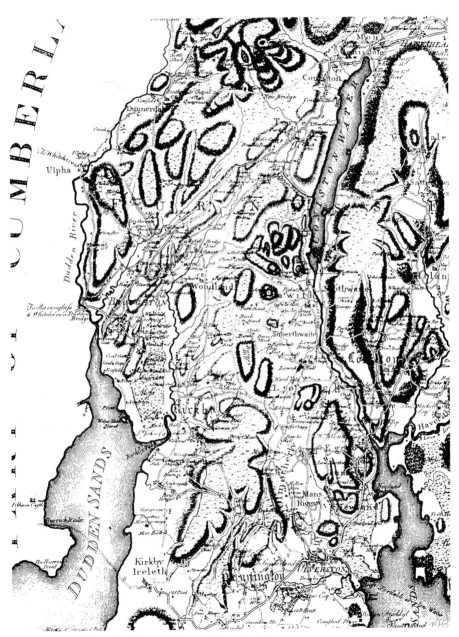

Extract from Yates's Map of Lancashire, 1786.

Extract from Ordnance Survey six-inch sheet showing Kirkby, edition of 1919.

X

The Ellen Rose Fieldhouse Collection

BD/F 1/1–6

1/1–6 Original records:

These few items are enclosed in a series of manila folders. The collection includes little other primary archival material, except where it has been fixed into the scrapbooks.

1/1	Folder of Friendly Society material, including membership proposals book for Kirkby Institution, 1843–1848; printed report of Executive Committee of National Independent Order of Oddfellows Friendly Society, November 1923; minutes for Loyal Kirkby Ireleth Lodge of the National Independent Order of Oddfellows Friend Society, 28 December 1938; printed booklet marked 'Order & Lecture Book' detailing catechisms and rituals of the Independent United Order of Mechanics, n.d.; manuscript book of 'Rules and regulations of the Kirkby Ireleth Friendly Society held at the Punch Bowl Inn,' 1848.	1843–1938
1/2	File of Kirkby-in-Furness Equitable Industrial Co-operative Society material, including *Short History*, 1861–1911, by John Woodhouse (Manchester 1912); account book (Arthur Fieldhouse), 1937–1962; cheque counterfoil book 1948–1953; letter from 'Florrie', 12 December 1966 about an error in Mrs. Fieldhouse's account; letter from President and Secretary of Kirkby Society regarding reorganisation of the Co-operative movement, 22 November 1968.	1912–1968
1/3	Kirkby Ireleth Girls Friendly Society: membership and subscription book, 1929–1945.	1929–1945
1/4	Kirkby-in-Furness Community Centre: pay-in counterfoil book, 1947– 1952; balance sheets 1952–1954.	1947–1954
1/5	Kirkby Ireleth Literary Society: syllabus cards including	1947–

	meetings, names of officers, etc., 1947–1959, 1966–1967; cheque counterfoil book, 1949–1955.	1967
1/6	Envelope with Kirkby Ireleth Drama Group material, including cash book, 1945–1951; script for *Ballet-Hoo*, n.d.; script for *The Deaf Man* by Aimée Scott (1935) with sheet of judge's comments on its performance at Furness & Cartmel Festival, 14 March 1951; receipted invoices with covering letter, 1950–1952.	1945–1952

BD/F 2/1–2/7

2/1–2/7 Thematic files

These series chiefly comprise short and neatly handwritten notes on the various specific topics indicated. The notes have generally been mounted on card, presumably for exhibition purposes. Occasionally, however, the files include research material in other formats, such as short sequences of correspondence or rough notes. The items are roughly grouped, and are enclosed in seven manila folders.

2/1	*The Village of Kirkby: general*	
	Taxes in Furness 1291–1565, and at marriage of John of Gaunt's eldest daughter.	1291–1565
	Plot by Alexander de Kirkby to kill Abbot of Furness, 1336	1336
	Note on will of John de Kirkby, 1600	1600
	Value of Rectory and Vicarage of Kirkby, 1650	1650
	Old bridges in Kirkby Ireleth, 1771	1771
	The Kirkby Family, from *The Antiquities of Furness* by T. West, 1774	1774
	Gill Beck and local field names, 1786	1786
	Depositions of Robert Wayles and others, 1582, quoted in T.D. Whitaker's *An History of Richmondshire*, 2 vols. (London, 1823)	1823
	Furness Churches, from Whitaker's *History of Richmondshire*, 1823	1823
	Beckside School, from *Topography and Directory of North Lancashire*, by P. Mannex & Co., 1866.	1866
	The Kirkby parish boundaries, from Mannex's *Directory*, 1866.	1866

The Druidical Circle; Kirkby Church; Seathwaite Chapel; Kirkby Ireleth manor, from *North Lonsdale Magazine*, September 1866.	1866
Furness Taxes, from J. Richardson's *Furness Past and Present*, Its History and Antiquities, 2 vols. (London, 1880).	1880
Inns in Kirkby Ireleth, 1882	1882
Kirkby: relics of prehistoric times (from Mannex *Directory*, 1882).	1882
'Kirkby-in-the News,' parts 1–4; the air crash on Kirkby Moor, 1939; the train crash at Kirkby Station, August 1939; the snow of February 1940; the flood of 1967.	1939–1967
Kirkby parish; history of the area; the Kirkby family; 1960.	1960
The position of newcomers in Kirkby society.	1969
Folklore regarding the use of black pippins from apples.	n.d.
Illegal marriages.	n.d.
The 'Kirk' above High Ghyll.	n.d.
The 'Kirk' above High Ghyll.	n.d.
The Kirkbys; Occupations; 20th Century changes; the Church; Kirkby family; Kirkby Hall; ancient customs.	n.d.
Land at Kirkby belonging to Furness Abbey.	n.d.
Medieval spellings of Furness towns and areas.	n.d.
Anonymous poem: 'My Cheer-Ups'; 23 November 1958.	1958
Kirkby place-names with first recorded use.	n.d.
The Penny Bridge Toll Bar, from W. White's *Furness Folk and Facts*, p. 11.	n.d.
A 16th Century Visitation to Kirkby Ireleth.	n.d.
Kirkby-in-Ireleth: manuscript notes on the name, manor, extent of parish; church building, etc.	n.d.
'Kirkby Snippets': a pot-pourri of facts about the village.	n.d.

2/2   *Dialect*

Variations on the name Kirkby, from T.D. Whitaker's *History of Richmondshire* (London, 1823).	1823
A Glossary of Lancashire dialect words, compiled by the Manchester Literary Club, 1875 (10 pages).	1875
Dialect names for Wool, and used in counting sheep, 1895.	1895
Name derivations for Duddon; Steers Pool; Otter Pool (Angerton); Lickle; based on E. Eckwall's *The Place Names of Lancashire*, (Manchester, 1922).	1922
'Some dialect words "Ta Deu Wid Sheep"', by J.T. Relph.	n.d.
List of assorted dialect phrases [4 pages].	n.d.
Poem: 'To mi Dawter on 'er twenty fost bothday'.	n.d.

2/3	*Farming*	
	Kirkby parish register entries relating to families from Hallsteads, 1754–1812.	1754–1812
	Tithes in Lamplugh, 1771 [2 copies].	1771
	Notes from Charity Commissioners report relating to Hallsteads Charity, 1820; details of distribution of the charity, 1902.	1820& 1902
	Entry for Angerton Moss, from *Victoria County History of Lancashire* (London, 1914).	1914
	Portfolio with lists of field names, plot numbers and areas of fields held as parts of the following farms: Ashlack Hall (covering letter 2 May 1966); Rectory Farm; High Ghyll House (covering letter 26 April 1966); The Marshfield, Chapels; Cross Beck, Angerton (covering letter dated 18 April 1966); Bank End Farm; Ghyll End Farm; Bayliff Ground Farm; Low Hall; Low Gill Farm; Kirkby Hall; Prospect farm; Bell Hall; Croglin; Pear Tree Farm; Moss House Farm (with covering letter); Moorhouse Farm; Beanthwaite Farm (covering letter 3 May 1966); Beckstones Farm (with covering letter); Dove Ford; High Bank House; Green Farm (with covering letter); letter from Wallend Farm unable to supply details. [Letters for a survey organised by Mrs. Fieldhouse]. Also list of Public Rights of Way (based on definitive map, 1966) and note of local Commons; 1966.	
	Notes on History of Marsh Grange, from details supplied by Mr. James Melville, September 1963.	1963
	List of field names, with acreages and tithes payable, for Gillbeck Farm (held by Mr. J. Shepherd); with plan.	n.d.
2/4	*The Kirkbys and Kirkby Hall*	
	Transcript of grant by William of Lancaster to William, son of Roger de Kirkby Ireleth of land in Dunnerdale and Seathwaite, c.1170–1184. [Original in Kuerdon MS]	c.1170
	Note about will of Henry Kirkby, died 1524.	1524
	List of Kirkby family entries in Torver parish registers, 1681–1801.	1681–1801
	Note on William Kirkby and repression of dissenters in 1684, taken from *Victoria County History of Lancashire*, 1914.	1684
	Abstract from Lancashire Record Office catalogue relating to Kirkby Mill (Holker Muniments); 1770–1776.	1770–1776
	Extract about Kirkby Hall from Annual Reports of *Barrow Naturalists' Field Club*, 1902–1904.	1902–1904

Description of four Kirkby family portraits from sale catalogue; estate of H.S. Cowper, Hawkshead, 1951.	1951
Notes about Kirkby family ancestors living in Ashton parish during the 15th Century (from Baines' *History of Lancashire*, 1824).	n.d.
Note about Ashlack Hall.	n.d.
Kirkby Hall: the structure (from J. Richardson's *Furness Past and Present*).	n.d.
Kirkby Manor: the boundaries, as noted in Kuerdon manuscripts.	n.d.
The Kirkbys and Furness Abbey, from *Victoria County History*.	n.d.
Feudal Customs attached to Kirkby Manor (from *History and Directory of Furness and West Cumberland* (1882).	n.d.
The Cross at Kirkby Hall.	n.d.
Notes on the manorial court under Victor Cavendish, Lord of the Manor; also on 'the Kirk' (stone circle).	n.d.
Note on vagrants at Kirkby Hall during the Tudor period.	n.d.
Note of The Civil War (from *Victoria County History*).	n.d.

2/5	*Local families*	
	List of certain Lancashire wills (Archdeaconry of Richmond) in collection at Somerset House, 1457–1680; abstracts of Lancashire wills from British Museum, 1531–1652.	1457–1680
	List of old Kirkby families, 1524–1697.	1524–1697
	Note: fragment of Kirkby Ireleth register, 1551.	1551
	Note: finding the above fragment during work on the Dalton registers.	1551
	List of commonly-recurring names in Kirkby register.	1681–1812
	The 'Twenty-four' of Kirkby parish, 1684.	1684
	Baptismal entries from Gillbeck, 1771–1802.	1771–1802
	Burial entries from Gillbeck, 1684–1801.	1684–1801
	Copy of conveyance of moieties of Gillbeck, from George Woodburne of Gillbeck, Kirkby Ireleth, to Henry Woodburne of Croglin, yeoman and Robert Kellett the Younger of Gillbeck, yeoman, 22 February 1691.	1691
	Note regarding men pressganged from North of the Sands, 1745.	1745
	Rough note of Woodburne family conveyances in Holker	1751–

Muniments (Lancashire Record Office) 1751–1781; note of bequest from John Bradfield of Kirkby to Thomas Woodburne, 1796.	1796
Typescript copy of will, 17 September 1766 and probate 1767 of will, 1767, of Roger Hunter of Soutergate. Bequests include:-	1766

– Thomas, his son: one cow; one mare; one bed and furniture; one chist used for malt; one cart and pair of wheels; two pewter dishes; one box with corn and hay; one large pot; one little iron pan.

– Mary, his daughter: one feather bed; two pewter dishes.

– Francis Matson: one pound.

'After the Reformation': a brief note regarding local apostates, from *Victoria County History*.	n.d.
Extracts from Furness Coucher Book regarding name Ashlack, with variants, and dates of use.	n.d.
Local occupations.	
Order to pay money for apprehending vagrants, and transcript of warrant to whip a vagrant out of the County of Lancashire.	n.d.

2/6	*St Cuthbert's Church, Kirkby Ireleth*	
	Inventory of church goods, 1553	1553
	Note from introduction to published Dalton-in-Furness registers, regarding finding of Kirkby register fragment (1551).	n.d.
	Notes from *Prelates and People of the Lake Counties* by C.M.L. Bouch (Kendal, 1948) concerning visitation of 1578; Commissioner's Visitation, 1633; taxes and income of benefice.	n.d.
	Inscription from old bell, as noted in *North Lonsdale Magazine*, July 1866.	1866
	Further extract regarding Kirkby church from *North Lonsdale Magazine*, September 1866.	1866
	Extract from Transactions of *Cumberland & Westmorland Antiquarian and Archaeological Society*, 1902, regarding church bells at Colton, Kirkby Ireleth, Broughton, Woodland and Seathwaite.	1901–1902
	Drawing of Old Saxon capitals, apparently from bell.	n.d.
	Reminiscences of Mrs. Jane Shaw regarding the bells. *c*.1902.	1902
	Guide to Kirkby Church by Ellen Rose Fieldhouse, 1958.	1958
	Note: Kirkby and its chapels.	n.d.

Seven sheets with water-colours and calligraphic text relating to the church.	n.d.
Envelope with notes and correspondence about the church bells.	n.d.
Calligraphic reproduction of Mrs. Fieldhouse's booklet on the church.	n.d.

2/7   *Miscellaneous*

Copy of an address by the Duke of Devonshire at opening of Barrow Docks, 1867.	1867
Three-page extract about discoveries in the Kirkby Ireleth area, from John Bolton's *Geological Fragments collected principally from Rambles among the rocks of Furness and Cartmel* (London, 1869).	1869
Diagrams with commentary from *Furness & West Cumberland Directory*: Settlement at Heathwaite Fell; Homesteads at Heathwaite; Stone Rings at Heathwaite (1882).	1882
Extract regarding Crossing the Sands, from *Rambles in the Lake Country and its Borders* by Edwin Waugh, (London, 1882).	1882
Extracts from articles: Mumming, including a version used in Dendron parish, by Rev. A.J. Humphries, (*Barrow Naturalists Field Club*, 1902–04); The 'Jolly Boys' pageant in Passion Week, (Lonsdale Magazine, 1821); composite version of the 'Jolly Boys' play by J. Coward, G. Campbell and – Walker, n.d.; script for 'St. George and the Dragon' from Rodney Bennet's *Lets Do a Play* (London, 1933); 'Jolly Boys' song from memory, by S. Shaw, 4 May 1966.	1821– 1966
Report: outing of North Lonsdale Field Club to Heathwaite Fell settlements and the Giant's Grave, 16 August 1907.	1907
'A Sorry Disappointment!' A Story about Thomas Woodburne, solicitor, Ulverston, from Mackereth's Furness Year Book, 1908.	1908
Note: The Furness Railway, *c.*1910.	*c.*1910
Extract on the Volunteer Movement 1860–1903, from *A Furness Military Chronicle* by Alfred Fell (Ulverston, 1937).	1937
Draft for lecture by Arthur Fieldhouse on 'The Roads of England' 20 January 1948; (includes extracts from *The Story of the Roads*, by C.H. Routledge, 1927).	1948

Note on John Matson, born 1760 (from *Biographical Dictionary of English Architects* 1660–1840 by H.M. Colvin).	1954
Child's essay: 'A visit to Hadrian's Wall', 1971.	1971
Children's essays: 'On coming to live in Kirkby' with notes on the village, 11 October 1974.	1974
Quotation from rules of Lamplugh Friendly Society.	n.d.
Note: 'Victorian Amusements'.	n.d.

BD/F 3

3/1–54 Personal Correspondence: general:

(To Ellen Rose Fieldhouse except where otherwise stated)

This section comprises a single file of letters, plus final sets of correspondence in three large envelopes. Many of the letters are answers to research enquiries. Some are copies supplied to Mrs. Fieldhouse from the postbag of Lewis Kirby in America and elsewhere. Certain of the items of more personal correspondence are subject to a 50 year closure period from their date of origin.

1	Letters from Frank Garstang, District Secretary of Workers' Educational Association, Robert E. Speirs, Secretary and Eric D. Gaudie, Chairman of Barrow branch (2 items) about resignation of Ellen Fieldhouse from post of Hon. Secretary and Hon. Treasurer to Barrow Branch, 26 July–2 December 1934.	1934
2	Receipt from George Whitfield, Barrow architect, for £30 to C. Sykes, Secretary of the Kirkby-in-Furness Community Centre for a survey, 7 November 1952.	1952
3	Lord Clitheroe of 45 Wilton Crescent, London, 7 May 1958, re Kirkby and Assheton families.	1958
4	F. Barnes of Barrow-in-Furness Public Library, 12 May 1958, re origin of names Kirkby and Ireleth.	1958
5	R.W. Crawshaw, P.R. Officer for British Railways, 11 September 1958, re the 1939 train crash at Kirkby-in-Furness station with recommended list of books on Furness Railway history.	1958
6	E. Brunskill, Assistant Librarian at York, 23 September 1958, re church bells.	1958
7	Robin A. Hill, 20 October 1958, re information about Kirkby Ireleth to be found on p. 1027 in James Torre's MS on Peculiars in the Minster Library, York.	1958

8	Correspondence Department of *News Chronicle* and *Daily Dispatch*, 8 December 1958, re Kirkby rail accident in 1939 [see BD/F 10/2].	1958
9	John Brelstaff, 20 December 1958, re school visit to Kirkby Church.	1958
10	John Taylor and Co., The Bell Foundry, Loughborough, 20 July 1959, to Rev. E.C. Whitaker, re information on the bells at Kirkby Ireleth Church.	1959
11	S.E. Sanderson, Lecturer in Folk Life Studies, University of Leeds, 5 February and 5 June 1963, re dialect and other tapes (2).	1963
12	Hilda Wayles of Barrow Naturalists' Field Club and Photographic Society, 17 March, 5 May, 1 September 1963 (3).	1963
13	J. Melville, 20 September 1963, re Cumberland and Westmorland Antiquarian and Archaeological Society outing to Kirkby Ireleth.	1963
14	Thel Atkinson of Moor View, Soutergate in Kirkby Ireleth, 23 November and 3 December re the date of the death of Thomas Postlethwaite.	1964
15	J.L. Kirby, 18 December 1964, to James Melville of Barrow-in-Furness, local historian, thanking him for use of the copy diary and battle accounts of Colonel Richard Kirby. [c.c.]	1964
16	Clyde W. Mason of New York, 21 May 1965, re Kirkby Ireleth parish register.	1965
17	J.L. Kirby to Noel Currer-Briggs, 8 July 1965, re purchase of Kirkby portraits. [c.c.]	1965
18	E. Jeffrey of Ravenstonedale, August–October 1965, and 10 February 1969 (10) with copies of replies by Ellen Fieldhouse (3) re Kirkby Ireleth parish map.	1965–1969
19	Clare Fell, President of the Cumberland and Westmorland Antiquarian and Archaeological Society, 22 April 1965–23 November 1972 (6).	1965–1972
20	E. Jeffrey of Kirkby Stephen, September 1965–October 1966 (4), re making of a map of Kirkby-in-Furness with the Kirkby family coat of arms and motto.	1965–1966
21	J.L. Kirby and E. Jeffrey of Ravenstonedale correspondence re making of map of Kirkby-in-Furness with Kirkby family arms and motto, November–December 1965, and April–July 1966 (11) [cc. and ph.)	1965–1966
22	Deputy Chief Constable of County Police H.Q., Hutton, Preston, Lancashire, 17 March 1966, re possible police station at Beckside, Kirkby Ireleth.	1966

23	Elizabeth Shepherd of Ghyll Beck, Kirkby Ireleth, 27 April 1966–19 August 1969 (5), re history of the farm.	1966–1969
24	J.L. Kirby, telegram, 14 May 1966, acknowledging arrival of Coat of Arms.	1966
25	Kirkby Co-operative Store, 12 December 1966, re the year's accounts.	1966
26	Letters and lists about research of Kirby family tree of 16–17th century. Correspondence between J.L. Kirby and Noel Currer-Briggs, July 1966, December 1972, November 1973, January 1976, July 1976 (6 items).	1966–1976
27	Secretary of North Lonsdale Society to J.L. Kirby welcoming him to the Society and enclosing a programme of lectures, 9 February 1967 [ph.]	1967
28	J.L. Kirby and G.C.L. de Jager, correspondence re the purchase of 2 portraits, August–October 1967 (4). [ph.]	1967
29	Reverend E.C. Whitaker, Vicar of Kirkby Ireleth to J.L. Kirby referring to offer of financial aid to the village church October 1967–March 1968 (9), [ph.]	1967–1968
30	J.L. Kirby and Peyton Skipwith correspondence, re a painting 'The Cornfield', August–September 1968, (3). [ph.]	1968
31	J.L. Kirby and J. Robinson correspondence re possible purchase of Ashlack Hall, September 1968–June 1972 (8), with article by Michael Hanson 'How High Can Farmland Prices Go', *Country Life*, (4 May 1972), 1118. [ph.]	1968–1972
32	The Curator of the Ruskin Galleries, Bembridge School, London, 3 February 1969, re H.S. Cowper sale catalogue in which Kirkby portraits appeared.	1969
33	Notes on Furness associations with the Virginia colony with accompanying letter from J.L. Kirby to N. Currer-Briggs, 31 March 1969. [c.c.]	1969
34	F. Barnes, of Barrow-in-Furness Public Library, 10 June 1969, re photocopying of newspaper items ordered.	1969
35	Secretary of Northern News Editor, *Daily Mail*, 23 July 1969, to R.H. Shuttleworth, Sheffield re 50th wedding anniversary of Mr. and Mrs. Holloway.	1969
36	Colin Knipe of Stourbridge, Worcestershire, 14 September 1969, re map of Kirkby Ireleth parish.	1969
37	J.L. Kirby to Noel Currer-Briggs, 5 November 1969 re genealogy of Kirby family in 17th century. [ph.]	1969
38	J.L. Kirby to Cumberland and Westmorland Antiquarian and Archaeological Society enclosing $25 donation, 7 January 1970. [ph.]	1970

39	Copy to City Archivist from Ellen Fieldhouse, 4 March 1970, enquiring into information about Gill Beck Farm, with reply from the Bristol Archives Office, 13 March 1970.	1970
40	C.R. Huddleston, editor of *Transactions of the Cumberland and Westmorland Antiquarian and Archaeological Society*, 21 March 1970 re possible talk at Gill Beck, 24 August 1970. (2).	1970
41	Receipts from Lakeland Dialect Society, 14 June 1970 for 10s 6d subscription by Ellen Fieldhouse, and for years 1970/71 for Cumberland and Westmorland Antiquarian and Archaeological Society.	1970
42	Application for membership to Cumberland and Westmorland Antiquarian and Archaeological Society for J.L. Kirby, 1 July 1970, proposed by E. Fieldhouse. [ph.]	1970
43	C.V. Knipe, 17 July 1970, re history of the Burlington Slate Quarries.	1970
44	Lord Wakefield of Kendal and J.L. Kirby, January 1971, re purchase of Ashlack Hall. (2).	1971
45	Noel Currer-Briggs, 8 January 1971, acknowledging receipt of Lewis Kirby's book on The Wigg Family.	1971
46	Mrs. M.M. Coyle of Manchester University Press, 24 June 1971, re Chetham books.	1971
47	J.L. Kirby to Noel Currer-Briggs, 10 August 1971, re Kirkby place names in Yorkshire and Lancashire. [ph.]	1971
48	J.L. Kirby and G.R. Elvey, correspondence, December 1971, including a short history of the Wigg Family 1390–1519. (2). [ph.]	1971
49	Donald Sykes, Treasurer of The Yorkshire Dialect Society, 4 July 1976, enclosing receipt for subscription. (Enclosed: three earlier letters between Mrs. Fieldhouse and the Society, 1972).	1972–1976
50	A.L. Wills, Divisional Librarian, expressing thanks for talk given to the Ulverston Library Society.	n.d.
51	Card from the Treasurer of the Cumberland and Westmorland Antiquarian and Archaeological Society.	
52	Envelope with brochure, correspondence etc. to J.L. Kirby about possible purchase of Seaton Hall estate, Bootle.	1973–74
53	Envelope with correspondence to J.L. Kirby about possible purchase of Burrow Hall, Kirkby Lonsdale 1974.	1974

54   Envelope with correspondence from Harry Coward of Regina, Saskatchewan about Coward/Johnson family history. (Refers to link between Coward family and Kirkby of Stonedykes and Gawthwaite, mid 18th Century). 5 January 1975–27 May 1976

BD/F 4

4/1/1–7 Personal Correspondence: Fieldhouse relatives, 1960's–1978

4/2/1–8 Personal Correspondence: Kirkby family, 1960's–1978

This section consists of a single file, with two small sets of purely personal corespondence. Restricted access applies for a 50 year period.

BD/F 5

5/1–266 Photocopies 16th–20th Century

The originals of many of the items in this lengthy section are at the Lancashire Record Office.

1   Fragment of Kirkby Ireleth register, 1551.   1551
2   *Will* of Richard Ayskew of March Grange, Kirkby Ireleth,   1551 co. Lancaster, made 25 November 1551. Bequests include:
         – wife [Gennet] estate during her widowhood,
         – William and John Askew, eldest sons, estate after wife's demise,
         – Margret and Jennet, daughters, 20 marks each on their marriage,
         – Alyxsander Tomlynson, 1 cow,
         – Robert Waylls, godson, 12d,
         – children of Thomas Hunter, 12d,
         – Roger and John, younger sons, £10 each,
         – John Mozes, 1 gemer hog.
         Witnesses: James Waylles, the elder; Robert Waylls; Thomas Yodell; Robert Kyrkbye.
3   Gaythorpe, Harper, 'A Bishop's Visitation to Furness in   1554 1554', *Transactions of the Cumberland and Westmorland Antiquarian and Archaeological Society*, NS.7, 269–72, with copy of part of original documents (1907).

4	*Wills and Inventories in the Archdeaconry of Richmond*, p. 190–91: extract including a transcript of the will of Anne Kirkbie, 12 September 1566.	1566
5	*Will* of William Kirkbi of Kirkby Ireleth, made 20 January 1580. Bequests include: – Robert, son, house and garden with commodities belonging to them, 10 shillings, – Rouland, son, great chest, 10 shillings, – John, son, 3s 4d, 10 shillings, – Elizabeth, daughter, one little arc, [2 copies with transcription].	1580/ 81
6	*Will* of Henry Kirkby made 19 February 1582. Bequests include: – James Wayles, nephew ⎱ 1 tenement lying in – Genat Kerkebye, daughter ⎰ Stainton, – (Sister's children in Soutergate), – Thomas Kellet, 1 cow and 2 ewes, 4 bushels of oats and 1 of barley, – Robart, servant, 20 geese, – John Wayles, 1 whiteheaded hefer, – John Kerkebye, goods moveable and unmoveable, – hoste – 6s and every child 12d, and 3 maids 6s each. Witnesses: Will[ia]m Torner, Rychard Scotte, Gylbart Scotte, Thomas Kellat.	1582/ 83
7	*Will* of Henry Kirkby of Dalton, co. Lancaster, made 12 February 1583. Bequests include: – William Kirkby, nephew, 20s after wife's death, – Thom' Banke, son of Matthew Banke, 6s 8d, – Thomas Richardson, son of Hen' Ricson', 1 lamb, – William Bolton, son of George Bolton of Rayth Mosse, 1 lamb, – Leonard Rallingson, Matthew Banke, William Ric'son and George Garnet, supervisors, 13s 4d, – William, brother, a pair of stadles. Witnesses: Matthew Banke, William Ricson', George Garnet, Ric' Banke and Ric' Garden. [with transcription].	1583/ 84
8	*Inventory* of goods of Henry Kirkby of Dalton, co. Lancaster, made 20 February 1583.	1583
9	*Transcript* of Customs of the Manor of Kirkby, circa 30 November 1585, made from a MS copy lent to the Holker Estate Office by Messrs. W.C. Kendall and Fisher of Ulverston (8 pages).	1585

10 *Will* of William Kerbie of Wodland, Kirkby Ireleth, co.   1587
    Lancaster, made 20 October 1587. Bequests include:
    – John Kirkby, son, one half of tenement and farmhold
    and other half after mother's death,
    – Richard Kirkby, son, £10 and the second best 'teme',
    – Richard, Isabell and Margaret Kirkby, children, £10,
    rest of goods to be equally divided,
    – Wife, 1 cow called Coppacke and other half of tenement
    and farmhold.
    Witnesses: Allan Apparke, John Dodson, Xaffer
    [Christofer] Shypherd and James Lancastre.
    [with transcription].

11 *Inventory* of William Kirkby, made 9 November 1587.   1587

12 *Will* of Robert Kirkby, Kirkby Ireleth, made 20 October 1588.
    Bequests include:
    – Elsabeth, sister, 6s 8d and £26. 8d. owed to her,
    – mother ⎱
    – John, brother ⎬
    – Jane, sister ⎪ rest of goods
    – Agnes, sister ⎰
    – James and Rolland, brothers, the covenant made with   1588
    Thomas Askew and Roger Garned.
    Witnesses: Thomas Clappa[m], James Hunt[er], Will[ia]m
    Cragge, Roger Cragge.

13 *Inventory* of goods of Robert Kirkbie, made 3 November   1588
    1588. [with transcription].

14 *Letters of Administration*, [13] November 1605, granted to   1605
    Elizabeth Matson of Cocken, co. Lancaster, widow, in
    respect of goods and chattels of Roger Matson, late
    husband deceased.

15 *Inventory* of the goods of Henry Kellet of Merebeck,   1615
    Kirkby Ireleth, co. Lancaster, made 13 November 1615
    [with transcription].

16 *Will* of Roger Kirkby the elder, made [1618]. Bequests   [1618]
    include:
    – Anne Kirkby, daughter ⎱
    – Roger, nephew and his son John ⎰ all goods
    – Anthony and Ralphe Kirkby, nephews £5,
    – Anne Sandforth, 20 noobles,
    – Thomas Fleminge and William Woodburne 40s each,
    – Margaret Rollinson, cousin, £3 1s 3d,
    – John Kirkby, trust of the house,
    – Daughter's children, 10 shillings each,
    – servants to have wages doubled.

	Witnesses: Thomas Fleminge, Richard [Parmiter], and Christopher Besbrowne.	
17	*Letters of Administration*, 23 February 1618, granted to Roger Kirkby of Kirkby Ireleth, co. Lancaster, knight, in respect of goods and chattels of Roger Kirkby, deceased.	1618/ 19
18	Probate copy of will of John Dampney of Kirkby Ireleth, co. Lancaster, made 16 September 1624.	1624
19	*Letters of Administration*, 20 February 1637, granted to Issabella Kirkby, of Lowhouse in Kirkby Ireleth, co. Lancaster, widow, in respect of goods and chattels of Henry Kirkby, late husband deceased.	1637/8
20	*Will* of John Kirkby of Copp, Kirkby Ireleth, co. Lancaster, made 1 March 1637. Bequests include:	1637/8

20
Will of John Kirkby of Copp, Kirkby Ireleth, co. Lancaster, made 1 March 1637. Bequests include:
– Jenet, wife ⎫
– Kathren and Margaret, daughters ⎬ estate equally divided
Witnesses: George Bayliffe, Thomas Askew, John Kirkby. [with transcription].

21	*Letters of Administration*, 27 February 1639, granted to Isabella Woodburne of Askew Gate, Kirkby Ireleth, co. Lancaster, widow, in respect of goods and chattels of Christopher Woodburne, late husband deceased.	1639/ 40
22	*Inventory* of the goods of John Kirkby of the Copp, Kirkby Ireleth, co. Lancaster, yeoman, made 8 October 1639.	1639
23	*Letters of Administration*, 17 May 1640, granted to Janet Woodburne of Sandside Kirkby Ireleth, co. Lancaster, widow in respect of goods and chattels of Christopher Woodburne, late husband deceased.	1642
24	*Will* of John Matson, of Scalebanke in Furneis, co. Lancaster, made 1 February 1657. Bequests include:	1657/8

24
Will of John Matson, of Scalebanke in Furneis, co. Lancaster, made 1 February 1657. Bequests include:
– Jo' Matson, eldest son, 2 messuages and tenements with appurtenances at Scalebancke commonly known as Gibson Tenement and Postlethwet Tenement,
– William, son, £40 from the above land on coming of age,
– Margret, daughter, £20 from the above land on coming of age and £20 from tenement at Pennington,
– Robert, son, messuages and tenements at Scalebank commonly known as Troughton Tenement, a coupe, a pair of wheels and a plow with irons, 1 bed, 1 table in the house belonging to Troughton Tenement,
– An, daughter, £60 from the tenement at Pennington,
– John, son, a coupe, a pair of wheels, a pair of cart wheels, a plow with irons, two tables and all the beds in the house except one.

Witnesses: James Sanderson, William Hart, Leo' Gibson, John Gibson.

25   *Will* of William Woodbourne of Gargreave, made 8 September 1660. Bequests include: **1660**
- Issabella, sister, Roger and Elizabeth Postelthwt, her son and daughter, and Thomas Askew, half of the goods which were to have gone to Elizabeth, wife, deceased, to be equally divided,
- Dorathie Cooke, servant, 15s and 1 chist.

Witnesses: John Postelthwt, Thomas Wailes.

26   *Will* of Ralph Kirkbie of Gargrave, Kirkby Ireleth, co. Lancaster, gentleman, made 1665. Bequests include: **1665**
- Jane [Jene] Kirkbie, mother, 1 bey mare, 10 young sheep,
- Ral. Hunter, godson, 5s,
- Elin. Woodburne (daughter of Henry Woodbourne) 5s,
- wives of William Bibie, John Woodburne, Jo' Hunter, Thomas godson, Ja' Nelson, Thomas Kirkbie, Jo' Singleton, Jo' Knipe, Thomas Woodburne, 12d each,
- Margrat Postlewet (daughter of Roger Postletwhet) 2s 6d.

Witnesses: James Dawson, William Woodburne.

27   *Inventory* of the goods of Ralph Kirkby of Gargreave, Kirkby Ireleth, co. Lancaster, made 5 March 1665 [with transcription].   **1665/6**

28   *Letters of Administration*, 24 April 1670, granted to Ann Matson, of Dalton in respect of goods and chattels of Thomas Matson, late father deceased.   **1670**

29   *Will* of Robert Matson of Corbei-in-Furness, co. Lancaster, yeoman, made 29 March 1672. Bequests include: **1672**
- Sir Thomas Preston of the Manor in Furness, baronet, 2 messuages and tenements and arable meadow and pasture in Corbei at annual rent 19/8d,
- Anne, daughter, 20s [wife of Thos. Cragge],
- Poor of parish of Dalton, 20s,
- Personal estate to be put up for public sale, half to Robert Matson, grandson, and half to be divided into 4 – eldest and youngest child and granddaughters.

30   *Agreement* of copyhold tenants of Kirkby Ireleth in dispute with Colonel Kirkby, co. Lancaster, 10 October 1681 [with transcription].   **1681**

31   *Conveyance*, 22 February 1690.   **1690/1**
1.   George Woodburne of Gilbecke in Kirkby Ireleth, co. Lancaster, yeoman.

2. Robert Kellet the younger of Gilbecke, yeoman.
Premises: one half messuage at Gilbeck in the manor of Kirkby Ireleth.
Consideration: £28.
Annual rent 2s 11d to Roger Kirkby, Lord of the manor, and 8d to the proctor.
Witnesses: George Woodburne, John Woodburne of Welhous, Henry Woodburne.

32   *Conveyance*, [—] February 1690.   1690/1
1. William Woodburne of Mearbeck in Kirkby Ireleth, co. Lancaster, butcher.
2. Robert Kellett of Scales, co. Lancaster.
Premises: messuage with barn at Mearbeck and 2 closes called the Crofts (boundaries given).
Consideration: £30.
Annual rent: 1s 2d.
Witnesses: Thos. Postlethwaite, Richd. Wayles, John Watter.
[Original deed, with transcription].

33   *Will* of John Brockbanke of Kirkby Ireleth, co. Lancaster,   1691
husbandman, made 17 September 1691. Bequests include:
– Agnes Brockbanke, niece, £5,
– John Brockbanke, nephew, £5,
– Robert Coulton's children, William, Agnes and Miles, 10s each,
– George, son, all husbandry gear,
– William Skelding, John Pennington, and Agnes Brockbanke, godchildren, 2s 6d each.
Witnesses: Miles Brockbanke, Thomas Wayles, Hugh Hunter.

34   *Conveyance*, 22 February 1691.   1691/2
1. George Woodburne of Gilbeck in Kirkby Ireleth, co. Lancaster, yeoman.
2. Henry Woodburne of Croglin in Kirkby Ireleth, co. Lancaster, yeoman.
Premises: one half messuage and tenement at Gillbeck within the manor of Kirkby Ireleth.
Annual Rent: 5s 10d. Consideration: £28.
Witnesses: Will[ia]m Woodburne, butcher, Robert Kellat, gent., John Woodburne, welhouse, William Coward.

35   *Letter*, 11 November 1692 from William Kirkby to the   1692
Keeper of the gaol at Lancaster, concerning Henry Nelson, charged with stealing. [with transcription].

36	Inventory of Hugh Hunter, 4 April 1699, late of Kirkby Ireleth, co. Lancaster, amounting to £20 14s 8d.	1699
37	*Notice* of sale of land, 24 September 1704 by Samuel Nelson of Broughton in Furness, co. Lancaster, yeoman. Premises: messuage etc. at Sandside in Kirkby Ireleth, co. Lancaster. Small modus in lieu of tythe.	1704
38	*Letters of Administration*, 8 November 1709, granted to Dorothy Hall of Beckside in Pennington, co. Lancaster, widow, in respect of goods and chattels of William Hall, late husband deceased.	1709
39	*Conveyance*, 1 February 1715. 1. John Simpson of Soutergate in Kirkby Ireleth, co. Lancaster, yeoman, and Margaret Simpson, widow, Kirkby Ireleth, co. Lancaster. 2. Roger Hunter of Soutergate, Kirkby Ireleth, bachelor. Premises: messuage, tenement etc. in Soutergate and land in Yeate Moss in Angerton Moss. Consideration: £40. Annual rent: 1s 10½d. Witnesses: John Woodburn, John Coulton, Abra[ha]m Rawlinson.	1715/16
40	'An account of the Manx Boats that came upon Duddon Sands', written by Thomas Briggs, 15 July and 5 October 1722.	1722
41	*Will* of Thomas Askew of Mosshouses in Broughton, co. Lancaster, yeoman, made 15 September 1731. Bequests include: – Thomas Askew, son, £1 1s, scaffolding and loose wood in the house, – Agnes, Elizabeth, Sarah and Ann, daughters, all other goods and chattels. Witnesses: Rob[er]t Askew, John Mayson, Tho[ma]s Nelson.	1731
42	*Letters of Administration*, 9 January 1738, granted to Ann Askew of Kirkby Ireleth, co. Lancaster, widow in respect of goods and chattels of Christopher Askew, late husband deceased.	1738/9
43	*Inventory* of goods of Christopher Askew, 9 January 1738.	1738/9
44	*Inventory*, 4 December 1739, of goods and chattels of Thomas Postelthwaite of Ireleth, co. Lancaster, amounting to £56 19s.	1739
45	*Letters of Administration*, 18 December 1739, granted to Anthony Postlethwait of Leeseby, co. York, clerk and	1739

Sarah Lesh of Kirkby Ireleth, co. Lancaster, widow in respect of goods and chattels of Thomas Postlewait, late of Kirkby Ireleth.

46   *Will* of Margaret Stephenson of Kelletground, Kirkby Ireleth, co. Lancaster, widow, made 5 February 1740. Bequests include: 1740/ 41
- Mary Dodson, £5,
- children of Mary Dodson, 5s each,
- Dorothy Stephenson, all goods and personal estate.

Witnesses: James Cowper, William Coward, James Waterson. Proved 13 March 1748 by J.S. Walker, surrogate.

47   *Letters of Administration*, 22 February 1741, granted to Tamer Wayles, widow, and James Wayles, husbandman, both of Grisebeck, and John Maddoc of Perbeike, milner, Kirkby Ireleth, co. Lancaster in respect of goods and chattels of James Wayles of Grisebeck, deceased.   1741/5

Witnesses: Henry Holmett, Tho[ma]s Elleray.

48   *Will* of Tamer Wayles, widow, of Grisebeck, made 24 February 1741. Bequests include: 1741/2
- Joel Park, brother, a clock,
- Isabell Penniton, half a crown,
- Christine Penniton, half a crown,
- Agnass Park, mother, apparell,
- Marey Higgin, god-daughter, a cap, hancorker and ribon,
- Sarey Higgin, sister-in-law, 1s,
- William Wayles, brother-in-law, 1s,
- James Wayles, father-in-law, 1s,
- Thomas Park, father, 1s.

Witnesses: Robert Glass, John Madocsword.

49   *Grant of tuition*, 9 September 1742, to Sarah Perry of Kirkby Ireleth, widow of William Lesh, co. Lancaster, yeoman, in respect of Edward Lesh, son of William Lesh of Ireleth, deceased, during his minority.   1742

50   *Mortgage*, 2 February 1743.   1743/4
1. Roger Parker of Mearbeck in Kirkby Ireleth, co. Lancaster, maltster.
2. Thomas Perry of Ireleth, co. Lancaster, yeoman.

Premises: messuage and tenement at Cockfish Hall in Kirkby Ireleth.

Annual rent: 13s 4½d to the Lord of the manor.

Consideration: £80.

51   *Letters of Administration*, 6 April 1743, granted to William   1743
        Nixon and James Sandham, both of Angerton, Kirkby
        Ireleth, co. Lancaster, husbandman, and George Butler
        of Old Barrow, co. Lancaster, husbandman, in respect of
        goods and chattels of William Nixon late father
        deceased.

52   *Inventory* of goods etc. of William Nixon, 6 April 1743,   1743
        amounting to £24 15s 10d.

53.   *Conveyance*, 1 March 1744.
        1. John Parker of Soutergate, Kirkby Ireleth, co. Lan-
        caster, yeoman. Agnes Parker of the same, widow, and
        James Addison of Farrhouses, Kirkby Ireleth, co. Lan-
        caster, yeoman.
        2. Hugh Dickinson of Cockfish Hall, Kirkby Ireleth, co.
        Lancaster, yeoman.
        Premises: copyhold land commonly called 'Shillfahrood'
        in the town field near Soutergate.
        Annual rent: 2½d to Lord of Manor, and 1½ to proctor for
        corn tythes.
        Consideration: £4 2s 6d.
        Witnesses: Thomas Benson, John Todd.

54   *Admittance*, 8 March 1744, by Thomas Bennet, Lord of the   1744/5
        Manor of Kirkby Ireleth, of William Middleton, son of
        the late William Middleton.
        Premises: messuage and tenements etc. called Fellyeat.
        Annual rent: 7s 2½d.
        Fine: £7 4s 2d.

55   *Will* of Robert Lancaster of Ringhouse in Woodland, near   1744
        Broughton, 1744 co. Lancaster, made 25 June 1744.
        Bequests include:
        – George, eldest son, stock of sheep, bedsteads and
        hangings of the 'new parlour',
        – James, second son, household goods, loose wood and
        sheep stock of the Grisdale estates, and all messuages and
        tenements at Grisdale and from which to pay Mary,
        youngest daughter, at 21st birthday £250,
        – Tamer, elder daughter, £200.
        – Mary, youngest daughter, £100,
        – Mary, wife, maintenance of children.
        Witnesses: Jo' [illegible], Tho[ma]s Postlethwaite, Wil-
        liam Postlethwait.

56   *Will* of David Forrester of Darry, co. Lancaster,   1745
        gentleman, made 2 September 1745. Bequests include:
        – William, son, 21 sheep,

- Mary, wife, £20,
- David, son, 2 spring calves for the use of his two sons John and Robert,
- John, son, 1 sheep,
- James, son, 1 black cow,
- Robert, son, remainder of estate.
Witnesses: William Heay, John McKeo.
With accompanying letter to E. Fieldhouse from R.W. Foster of Pennsylvania, 20 September and 11 October 1970.

57	*Land Tax Bill* for Kirkby Ireleth, 1746.	1746
58	*Will* of William Kirkby of Ashlack Hall, Kirkby Ireleth, co. Lancaster, made 26 January 1746. Bequests include:	1746

- William Comber Kirkby, son, 50 sheep from Knitlton Farm, 50 sheep from Burney Farm, 8 sheep from Ashlack Estate, all family pictors in Ashlack House, interest from a bond of £500,
- James Kirkby, Johanna Kirkby, Sarah Kirkby, daughters, residue of estate and appointed executors.
Witnesses: John Moss of Bourney, Thomas Postlethwaite of Doveford, Tho[ma]s Nelson of Sandside.
[with transcription].

59   *Conveyance*, 10 February 1747.   1747
1. Roger Parker of Meerbeck in Kirkby Ireleth, co. Lancaster, yeoman.
2. John Shepherd of Kirkby Ireleth, yeoman, and John Todd of Swarthmoor, co. Lancaster, maltster.
Premises: messuage and tenement at Cockfish Hall in Kirkby Ireleth.
Annual rent to the Lord of the Manor: 13s 6½d.
Reservation to the customs of the manor.
Consideration: £60.

60   *Mortgage*, 2 February 1748.   1748/9
1. Roger Parker of Mearbeck, Kirkby Ireleth, co. Lancaster, maltster.
2. William Ormandy of Mansriggs, Ulverston, co. Lancaster, elder.
Premises: messuage and tenement of Cockfish Hall.
Annual rent: 13s 4½d.
Consideration: £110.
Yearly interest: £4 per £100.
Endorsement: receipt of interest due 1 February 1753,
           :   note on division of property after execution of will of 2, 5 July 1770,
           :   settlement of accounts 13 February 1777.

Witnesses: James Lindow, John Shepherd, Tho[ma]s Nelson.

61   *Will* of Agnes Coward, widow, of Stonedikes in   1748/9
Subberthwaite, co. Lancaster, made 18 February 1748.
Bequests include:
– Mary Ormundy, niece, £10,
– Agnes Addison, niece, £10,
– Anne Higgin, niece, £10,
– Jane Middleton, niece, £10,
– Elizabeth Beck, servant, £30,
– Edward Wellson, cousin, £10,
– John Beck, kinsman, £5,
– William Cragge, kinsman, £15,
– John Cragge, kinsman, £15,
– James Cragge, kinsman, £15,
– Dorothy Cragge, kinswoman, £15,
– Margaret Cragge, kinswoman, £15,
Witnesses: John Taylor, Jeremiah Coward, James Waterson.

62   *Inventory* of estate of Margaret Stephenson of Whatehead,   1748
Coulton, co. Lancaster, widow, 4 March 1748.

63   *Inventory* of goods, chattels, and credits of Agnes Coward,   1749/
10 February 1749.   50

64   *Letters of Administration*, 23 February 1749 granted to   1749/
Eleanor Cragg of Broughton, co. Lancaster, spinster and   50
John Taylor of Stone Dykes, Ulverston, yeoman, in
respect of goods and chattels of Agnes Coward late of
Stone Dikes, widow, deceased.

65   *Will* of Eliner Coward of Gawthwaite, co. Lancaster,   1749/
widow, made 4 January 1749. Bequests include: 50
– William Fleming the elder, of Pennington, £6,
– John Denny of Ragidgil, £6,
– Jane Hill of Rosside, £6,
– Thomas Greenwood, nephew, £2 10s,
– Bridget Greenwood, niece, £2 10s.
Witnesses: Francis James, William Askew, Leonard Askew.

66   *Inventory* of goods of John Parker of Soutergate, 28   1749/
February 1749.   50

67   *Letters of Administration*, 3 March 1749, granted to Agnes   1749/
Newby, sister of the late Robert Kellet, and John   50
Newby, yeoman, both of Haveridge, co. Cumberland,
and Henry Coulton of Kirkby Ireleth, yeoman, in
respect of goods and chattels of Robert Kellet deceased,
of Kirkby Ireleth.

68	*Inventory* of the goods of Robert Kellet, 3 March 1749.	1749/50
69	*Renunciation of Administration* by Ann Parker of Soutergate in Kirkby Ireleth of the effects of John Parker, late blacksmith, to Richard Ormandy of Broughton, carpenter, principal creditor. 21 March 1749.	1749/50
70	*Letters of Administration*, 24 March 1749, granted to Richard Ormandy, principal creditor, and Ralph Gawith, both of Broughton, co. Lancaster in respect of goods and chattels of John Parker deceased of Soutergate, blacksmith. Witness: John [Laury].	1749/50
71	*Letters of Administration*, 24 March 1749, granted to Richard Ormandy, house carpenter, and William Walters, surgeon, both of Broughton, co. Lancaster, and Nicholas Braysbrown of Troughton Hall, husbandman, co. Lancaster, in respect of goods and chattels of John Parker of Soutergate, Kirkby Ireleth, deceased.	1749/50
72	*Will* of William Coward of Toad Hole in Kirkby Ireleth, co. Lancaster, yeoman, made 31 August 1750. Bequests include: – James, brother, 2 freehold messuages etc. at Gawthwaite, – Joseph, Jeremiah, Benjamin, brothers, £15 each, – Ann, sister, £15. Witnesses: George Postlthwaite, Mary Postlethwaite, John Kendall.	1750
73	*Inventory* of the estate of William Coward, of Toad Hole in Kirkby Ireleth, co. Lancaster, 14 September 1750.	1750
74	*Will* of Jane Ormandy of Hill, Kirkby Ireleth, co. Lancaster, widow, made 5 December 1750. Bequests include: – Elisabeth, daughter, £2 8s, – Mary, daughter, £2 4s, – Margaret, daughter, £3, – Jane, daughter, £4, – Alice, daughter, £4, – Thomas, son, rest of the estate. Witnesses: Margaret Nelson, Agnes Bourns, Tho[ma]s Nelson. Will executed 30 March 1756.	1750
75	*Letters of Administration*, 29 April 1751, granted to Jane Coward, widow, and John Taylor, yeoman, both of Stonedykes, and James Denny of Lane End in Lowick, husbandman, in respect of goods and chattels of Jeremiah Coward, husband deceased.	1751
76	*Inventory* of goods of Jeremiah Coward, 4 February 1750, amounting to £135.	1750/51

77	*Letters of Administration*, 11 May 1752, granted to Elizabeth Dixon of Kirkby Ireleth, co. Lancaster, widow, and John Thorniberow of Kirkby Ireleth, labourer, and Thomas Askew, tailor, of Kirkby Ireleth, in respect of goods and chattels of William Dixon late of Kirkby Ireleth, husband deceased.	1752
78	*Inventory* of goods of William Dixon of Beckside in Kirkby Ireleth, 6 May 1752.	1752
79	*Will* of Richard Woodburne of Shellfleet, Kirkby Ireleth, co. Lancaster, made 13 May 1752. Bequests include: – William, son, 5s, – Henry, son, £75, – James Nuby, servant, £1, – Thomas, son, personal estate. Witnesses: William Wilson, Francis James, Tho[ma]s Nelson.	1752
80	*Inventory* of goods of Richard Woodburne, 16 May 1752.	1752
81	*Conveyance*, 22 January 1752. 1. William Towerson, soldier belonging to William Hickman, Lieutenant Colonel in the Royal Regiment of Welsh Fusiliers commanded by Lieutenant General Husk, and Ann Towerson of Rawfould in Dunerdale, Kirkby Ireleth, co. Lancaster, widow. 2. Thomas Dickinson of Cockfish Hall in Kirkby Ireleth, co. Lancaster, waler. Premises: tenement in Soutergate Town Field by the quickwood adjoining Cockfish Hall field, and a parcel of land 'Kempgarth' adjoining Roger Parker's orchard at Sandside (boundaries noted). Annual rent to the Lord of the Manor 1s 6d and 2d for tythe corn. Consideration: £26. Witnesses: W[illia]m Cooper, William Ormandy, Thomas Ormandy, John Postlethwaite.	1753
82	*Letters of Administration*, 2 March 1753, granted to William Fleming of Greenmoss House, and John Denny of Ragesgill, and Thomas Towerson of Canon House, all in Pennington, co. Lancaster in respect of goods and chattels of Elinor Coward deceased.	1753
83	*Letters of Administration*, 1 June 1753, granted to Margaret Woodburn of Soutergate, Kirkby Ireleth, co. Lancaster, widow, and John Todd of Ulverston, maltster, in respect of goods and chattels of John Woodburn late of Soutergate, husband deceased.	1753

84	*Inventory*, 28 May 1753, of goods of John Woodburn of Soutergate.	1753
85	*Grant of tutition*, 6 June 1753, granted to William Walters of Broughton-in-Furness, co. Lancaster, surgeon, and Richard Atkinson of Kirkby Ireleth, butcher, in respect of Isaac Woodburn, son of John Woodburn of Kirkby Ireleth, deceased, during his minority.	1753
86	*Inventory* of goods and chattels of Joseph Millner of Grisebeck, Kirkby Ireleth, co. Lancaster. 15 October 1753.	1753
87	*Will* of Joseph Millner, 30 July 1753. Bequests include: – Ann, wife, all personal estate. Witnesses: Tho[m]a Nelson, Edward Askew.	1753
88	*Letters of Administration*, 19 October 1753, granted to Ann Millner of Grisebeck, Kirkby Ireleth, co. Lancaster, widow, and Richard Hobson, Kirkby Ireleth, husbandman, in respect of goods and chattels of Joseph Millner late of Grisebeck, husband deceased.	1753
89	*Will* of John Askew of Mosshouses in Broughton, co. Lancaster, made 12 January 1755. Bequests include: – Thomas Hunter of Ulverstone, kinsman, £30, – Elizabeth Taylor, wife of John Taylor, £30, – Ann Woodburne, wife of William Woodburne, of Dalton, £30, – Thomas Kirkby, son of Henry Kirkby, a chist and half of his sheep, – Agnes Kirkby, daughter of Henry Kirkby, a chist and half of his sheep, – Henry Kirkby, remainder of personal estate. Witnesses: John Long, Tho[ma]s Strickland.	1755
90	*Inventory* of goods, chattels etc. of John Askew of Moss Houses, made 30 January 1755.	1755
91	*Letters of Administration*, 31 January 1755, granted to Henry Kirkby of Mosshouses, husbandman, and Thomas Nelson of Sandside, both of Kirkby Ireleth, co. Lancaster, yeoman, in respect of goods and chattels of John Askew late of Mosshouses.	1755
92	*Will* of Andrew Barrow of Fellyeat, Cartmel, co. Lancaster, yeoman, made 6 February 1755. Bequests include: – Margaret, wife, use of house and goods during her widowhood, – William, son, freehold land, tenements near Fellyeat, long table, 2 pairs of bedstocks, 5 chests. – Richard, son, personal estate plus £100,	1755

- Margaret, daughter, £100,
- Elliner, daughter, £100,
- Mary, daughter, 2s 6d,
- Anne, daughter, (wife of William Jopson), 2s 6d,
- Elizabeth, daughter, (wife of Thomas Dickinson), 2s 6d.
Witnesses: Thomas Braithwaite, Thomas Michaelson, Rob[er]t Michaelson.

93   *Inventory* of goods and chattels of Andrew Barrow, late of   1756
Flookburgh, Cartmel, co. Lancaster, made 5 January 1756.

94   *Letters of Administration*, 8 January 1756, granted to   1756
Margaret Barrow of Flookburgh, co. Lancaster, widow,
and John Braithwaite of Fell Yeat, farmer, in respect of
goods and chattels of Andrew Barrow, late of Flookburgh, husband deceased.

95   *Letters of Administration*, 30 March 1756, granted to   1756
Thomas Ormandy of Liverpool, co. Lancaster, mariner,
in respect of goods and chattels of Jane Ormandy late of
Hill, Kirkby Ireleth.

96   *Will* of Henry Hunter of Bankhouse, Kirkby Ireleth, co.   1755
Lancaster, made 27 December 1755. Bequests include:
- Mary Hunter, wife, £40,
- Thomas Hunter, nephew, £20,
- Margaret Hunter, niece, £20,
- Elisabeth Hunter, £20,
- John Mayson of Soutergate, the elder, £20,
- John Mayson of Soutergate, the younger, £20,
- Thomas Mayson of Whitehaven, £20,
- Elisabeth Fell, sister, £10,
- Mary Holm, servant, £5.
Witnesses: Lanclott Shepherd, Tho[ma]s Nelson.

97   *Inventory* of the goods etc. of Henry Hunter of Bankhouse,   1756
Kirkby Ireleth, co. Lancaster, 1 March 1756.
Witnesses: Tho[ma]s Nelson, William Woodburn, Wil-
liam Postlethwaite.

98   *Letters of Administration*, 17 March 1756, granted to Mary   1756
Hunter of Bankhouse, widow, and John Mayson of
South Gate, husbandman, both of Kirkby Ireleth, co.
Lancaster, in respect of goods and chattels of Henry
Hunter late of Bankhouse, husband deceased.

99   *Mortgage*, 23 January 1758.   1758
1. John Kellet of Gillbeck, Kirkby Ireleth, co. Lancaster,
yeoman.
2. Agnes Stewardson, Ann Kellet, Margret Kellet,
daughters of John Kellet.

26

Premises: messuage, tenement at Gillbeck, with all rights belonging to the custom of the manor and Lordship of Kirkby Ireleth, paying annual rent of 8s 3d to the Lord of the Manor and annual sum of 3s 6d for corn tythe money.
Witnesses: Tho[ma]s Nelson, John Bradley, William Wayles.

100   *Will* of Thomas Askew of Fellyeate, Cartmel, co. Lancaster, gentleman, made 1 February 1763. Bequests include: 1763
- John, eldest son, 10 guineas,
- Margaret, Jane and Ann, daughters, £100,
- Thomas, son, messuages, lands etc. at Birkby, Cartmel and at Fellyeate,
Witnesses: William Robinson, Mary Massicks, U. Richardson.

101   *Will* of Roger Hunter of Soutergate, Kirkby Ireleth, co. Lancaster, yeoman, made 17 September 1766. Bequests include: 1766
- Thomas Hunter, son, 1 cow and 1 mare, 1 bed and furniture,
- Mary Hunter, daughter, 1 feather bed, clothes, 2 pewter dishes,
- Frances Matron, £1.

102   *Proof* of a Will of Roger Hunter late of Soutergate Kirkby Ireleth, co. Lancaster, admitted before Rev. Stephen Sutton, clerk and surrogate on 25 May 1767.   1767

103   *Conveyance*, 16 June 1767.   1767
1. Thomas Dickinson of Wellhouse, Broughton-in-Furness, co. Lancaster, yeoman.
2. Samuel Knite of Cockfish Hall, Kirkby Ireleth, co. Lancaster, husbandman.
Premises: messuage, tenement etc. at Cockfish Hall and grounds at Angerton Moss.
Annual rent: 5s 7d to the Lord of the Manor, and 1s 6d to the Rector of Kirkby Ireleth for corn tythe, and 12s 6d for the premises at Angerton Moss.
Consideration: £180.
Witnesses: Lanclott Shepherd, Thomas Nelson.

104   *Mortgage*, 17 June 1767.   1767
1. Samuel Knite of Cockfish Hall, Kirkby Ireleth, co. Lancaster, husbandman.
2. Thomas Dickinson of Wellhouse, Broughton-in-Furness, co. Lancaster, yeoman.

Premises: messuage, tenement etc. at Cockfish Hall and grounds at Angerton Moss.

Annual rent: 5s 7d to the Lord of the Manor, and 1s 6d to the Rector of Kirkby Ireleth for corn tythe and 12s 6d for premises at Angerton Moss.

Consideration: £180.

Witnesses: Lanclott Shepherd. Thomas Nelson.

105	*Inventory* of goods and chattels of William Lindow of Hawkswell, Ulverston, co. Lancaster, deceased, made 13 December 1768.	1768
106	*Grant of tuition*, 19 January 1769, granted to Ann Lindow of Hawkswell, Ulverstone, widow, and James Lindow of Broughton-Beck, Ulverstone, yeoman, both of co. Lancaster, in respect of Phebe, Mary, Anne, William, Thomas, James, children of William Lindow deceased, husband of Anne Lindow, during their minority.	1769
107	*Letters of Administration*, 19 January 1769 granted to Anne Lindow of Hawkswell, widow, and Samuel Towers of Broughton Beck, yeoman, and James Lindow of Broughton Beck, yeoman, Ulverston, co. Lancaster, in respect of goods and chattels of William Lindow late of Hawkswell, husband deceased.	1769
108	*Letters of Administration*, 8 November 1769, granted to Dorothy Hall, widow of Beckside in Pennington, co. Lancaster, and Thomas Hall of Colton, in respect of goods and chattels of William Hall, late of Beckside, husband deceased.	1769
109	*Inventory* of William Hall of Beckside, Kirkby Ireleth, co. Lancaster, 7 November 1769.	1769
110	*Rental* of Kirkby Ireleth Demesne for the year 1770, amounting to £327 7s.	1770
111	*Mortgage*, 13 June 1770.	1770; 1780

1. Roger Parker of Cockfish Hall in the manor of Kirkby Ireleth, co. Lancaster, yeoman.

2. Mary Ormandy of Mansriggs, co. Lancaster, spinster.

Premises: land at Cockfish Hall in the manor of Kirkby Ireleth.

Consideration: £70.

Witnesses: James Fell, John Addison, James Lindow, Thomas Petty [original in Prospect Estate papers].

Endorsement: 13 February 1780 re accounts of 1, witness William Ormandy.

: Receipt 13 February 1783 for sum £243 1s 4d.

112	*Rental* for land within the Manor of Kirkby Ireleth for	1770

	Christmas 1770 and 25 March 1771 – includes list of customary tenants, free rents, cottage rents, intack rents.	
113	*Valuation* of the lordship of Kirkby, according to Lord Mulgrave's proposal for enfranchising the tenants.	1772
114	Page showing 'An Account of the Expenses of repairing the buildings and fences on the Estate of the Right Honorable Lord John Cavendish at Kirkby Ireleth', 1772.	1772
115	*Valuation* of the Lordship of Kirkby (excluding the slate quarries) by J. Robinson, steward, 18 January 1772.	1772
116	*Account* of woods cut in Kirkby Ireleth in the grounds belonging to William Harts, William Lancaster, James Ferguson, John Dodson, William Postlethwaite, 24 July 1773.	1773
117	*Conveyance*, 19 January 1774.	1774

117   *Conveyance*, 19 January 1774.   1774
1. William Woodburn of Wellhouse, Kirkby Ireleth, co. Lancaster, waller.
2. John Woodburn of Wellhouse, Kirkby Ireleth, co. Lancaster, yeoman.
Premises: tenement called Long Dale, Knepster Rood, New Meadow (boundaries given) in the Manor of Kirkby Ireleth.
Consideration: £67 11s.
Witnesses: Thomas Woodburn, John Todd, Nicholas Todd [original in Prospect Estate Papers BSUD/D].

118   *Letter of Administration*, 3 March 1774, granted to Margaret Higgin of Nedderhouses, Ulverston, widow, and Edward Higgin, farmer, Ulverston, and Reginald Strickland of Rusland, Coulton, yeoman, all of co. Lancaster, in respect of goods and chattels of John Higgin, late of Nedderhouses, husband deceased.   1774

119   *Inventory* of John Higgin of Nedderhouses, Ulverston, yeoman, made 28 February 1774.   1774

120   *Will* of Thomas Nelson of Sandside, Kirkby Ireleth, co. Lancaster husbandman, made 25 March 1774. Bequests include: 1774
– Henry and John, sons, £60 each,
– Mary Parker, daughter, £60,
– grandchildren, £20 to be divided equally,
– Margaret Nelson, wife, all rents and profits of land in Sandside and Angerton Moss, and all personal estate and residue.
Witnesses: Lancelot Shepherd, John Shepherd, Agnes Shepherd.

	Probate date, 1 April 1776. Proved before Rev. Thomas Pearson, clerk and surrogate, 1 April 1776.	
121	*Will* of James Coward of Gawthwaite, Ulverston, co. Lancaster, yeoman, made 16 June 1774. Bequests include: – Elizabeth Sand, daughter, messuage, lands and premises now occupied by William Sand, for life, or to be paid £4 yearly in lieu of property, – Anne Wilson, daughter, £80, – Mary Quail, daughter, annual sum of £2 16s and after her decease £150 to be divided between her children, – Margaret, wife, 1 bed, furniture and personal estate, – John, son, real estate. Witnesses: Margaret Jinkson, Joseph Coward, J[oh]n Kendal.	1774
122	*Inventory* of goods and chattels of James Coward, 3 September 1774.	1774
123	*Mortgate*, 17 August 1775. 1. Roger Parker of Cockfish Hall in the manor of Kirkby Ireleth co. Lancaster, yeoman. 2. John Robinson, Ulverston, co. Lancaster, gentleman. Premises: messuages at Cockfish Hall, and land at Angerton Moss commonly called 'One Share and a Quarter', 15 customary acres. Consideration: £80. Annual rent: 14¾d. Witnesses: M. Fitzgerald, John Wenningsons. [Originals in Prospect Estate papers: BSUD/D].	1775
124	*Proof* of a Will of Thomas Nelson of Kirkby Ireleth, co. Lancaster, 1 April 1776. Admitted before Rev. Thomas Pearson, clerk and surrogate.	1776
125	*Mortgage*, 8 February 1776. 1. Roger Parker of Cockfish Hall in the manor of Kirkby Ireleth, co. Lancaster, yeoman. 2. Joseph Harrison of Ulverston, cornfactor. Premises: messuage at Cockfish Hall containing 15 customary acres, and at Angerton Moss commonly called 'One Share and a Quarter'. Consideration: £180. Witnesses: J[oh]n Robinson, H. Fitzgerald. [Original in Prospect Estate papers: BSUD/D]. Annual customary rent: 14¾d. Endorsement: 20 February 1783; receipt for £230 8s.	1776

126   *Rental* of the manor of Kirkby Ireleth, the slate quarries   1776
and the mills in the lands of the customary tenants and
on the common pasture for 1776.

127   *Will* of William Coward of Grofacragg, Ulverston, co.   1776
Lancaster, husbandman, made 22 January 1776.
Bequests include:
– James, son, all estate at Grofacragg and all personal estate
     except that stated,
– William, son, the clock and chest of drawers in the
     parlour and £80,
– Ann and Jane, daughters, £60 each.
Witnesses; William Geldart, Jane Geldart.

128   *Will* of James Kirby of Stonedykes in Suberthwaite,   1776
Ulverston, co. Lancaster, yeoman, made 8 July 1776.
Bequests include:
– William Kirkby, brother, sheep stocks on the estate at
     Burney (otherwise known as Burney End), Watery eels
     and all goods and household furniture,
– Margaret Jackson, niece, 5 guineas,
– Agnes Redhead, niece, 5 guineas,
– Mary Davis, cousin, 5 guineas,
– Margaret Wakes, niece, $2\frac{1}{2}$ guineas,
– Agnes Miller, niece, $2\frac{1}{2}$ guineas,
– Robert Redhead, brother, 2 guineas,
– Agnes Atkinson, god-daughter, 1 guinea,
– Robert Nelson, cousin, 1 guinea,
– Agnes, wife, use of the mahogany writing desk, 2 large
     silver spoons, and residue of personal estate.
Witnesses: John Taylor, J[oh]n Kendal.

129   *Inventory* of James Kirkby of Stonedykes in Suberthwaite,   1777
Ulverston, deceased, amounting to £440 19s. 8 July
1777.

130   *Admittance*, 27 May 1777, by John Robinson, gentleman,   1777
steward of the manor court of Kirkby Ireleth (held for
Lord John Cavendish, lord of the manor) held at
Beckside, of John Newby.
Premises: messuage and outhouse and certain parcels of
land at Merebeck.
Annual rent: 1s 5¾d.
Fine: 9s 7d.

131   Page from manorial records at Court Baron relating to   1777
John Newby becoming tenant to Lord Cavendish, 27
May 1777.

         Those subscribing in Kirkby Manor to purchase the   1778

freedom of their estate, terms suggested. 28 March 1778.

132   *Will* of William Miniken of Grofacragg, Ulverston, co.   1779
Lancaster, husbandman, made 13 September 1779.
Bequests include:
– Bridget, wife, messuage, tenements and real estate in Grofacragg to the use of, and rents during her life, and after to John, son, and personal estate,
– Jane Hully, daughter, £100,
– Elmer Miniken, daughter, £100,
– Margaret Miniken, daughter, £100.
Witnesses: James Coward, William Coward, J[oh]n Kendal.

133   *Inventory* of William Miniken, amounting to £51, 30   1780
August 1780.

134   *List* of tenants in the Manor of Kirkby Ireleth who   1780
purchased the enfranchisement of their tenements in January 1780 and prior to the 31 December 1780, and an account of the rents and purchase money paid by them respectively. (2 copies).

135   *Lease* (part of Lease and Release), 8 January 1780.   1780
1.   Lord John Cavendish, lord of the manor of Kirkby Ireleth, co. Lancaster.
2.   John Newby of Lanurigg, co. Cumberland.
Premises: messuage, lands etc at Mearbeck, in the manor of Kirkby Ireleth comprising a messuage, outhouses, gardens, etc. Rservation of rights to oak timber, and all seigniary, royalties and manorial rights.
Term: 1 year.
Consideration: 5s.

136   *Conveyance* (cancelled), 30 November 1780,   1780
1.   Henry Nelson of Arnaby, Millom, co. Cumberland, husbandman and John Nelson of Soutergate in manor of Kirkby Ireleth, co. Lancaster, waller, and Mary Parker of Soutergate aforesaid, widow (sons and daughter of late Thomas Nelson of Sandside.
2.   Samuel Nelson of Muncaster House, co. Cumberland, yeoman.
Premises: messuage and tenement at Sandside, and in manor of Kirkby Ireleth.
Recital of earlier Indenture, 17 March 1774.
Customary rent: 9s 6½d and cottage rent 8d.
Consideration: £200.
Witnesses: J[oh]n Robinson, Jo' Postlethwaite.

137	*Mortgate* (cancelled), 1 December 1780.	1780;
	1. Samuel Nelson of Muncaster House, co. Cumberland, yeoman.	1782
	2. Henry Cherington of Broughton, co. Lancaster, joiner.	

Premises: messuage and tenement at Sandside in the manor of Kirkby Ireleth.

Annual rent: 9s 6½d and cottage rent of 8d. Consideration: £200.

Witnesses: John Atkinson, John Robinson.

[Original in Prospect Estate papers, BSUD/D].

Applied Seal.

Endorsement, 7 November 1782, receipt for £206 15s.

138	*Receipts* (6) for legacies from a will by Samuel Nelson, 1 December 1780 to Mary Parker, her children, Henry Nelson's children, John Nelson's children.	1780
139	*Extracts* from Soutergate Marsh Book for the years 1781–1865 (59 pages).	1781–1865
140	*Lease*, 23 January 1782.	1782
	1. Lord John Cavendish of Manor of Kirkby Ireleth, co. Lancaster.	
	2. Samuel Nelson of Muncaster, co. Cumberland, yeoman.	

Reservation of manorial rights and royalities, fishing rights, mining etc.

Term 1 year.

Premises: messuage and tenement at Sandside in the manor of Kirkby Ireleth and ground called the Crewell, the Crewell Parish Highfield, Longfield, Newfield, Gatelands, Shilfadales and Bo Horns etc.

Consideration: 5s.

Annual rent: 1 peppercorn.

Seal.

141	*Land Tax Till* for Kirkby Ireleth, 1782.	1782
142	*Will* of Joseph Hart of Kirkby Ireleth, co. Lancaster, gentleman, made 26 October 1782. Bequests include:	1782

- Margaret, eldest daughter, (wife of Thomas Tyson) £200,
- Agnes, daughter, (wife of John Belman) £100,
- James Fell, grandson (son of Agnes) £50,
- Margaret Fell, granddaughter (daughter of Agnes) £50 at 21 years,
- Sarah, daughter (wife of George Brockbank) £200.

Witnesses: Margaret Woes, William Tyson.

143   *Conveyance*, 13 February 1783.   1783
        1. Roger Parker of Soutergate, Kirkby Ireleth, co. Lancaster, yeoman.
        2. Thomas Knight of Cockfish Hall, Kirkby Ireleth, waller.
        Premises: tenement of Quickwoods Close near Cockfish Hall within the manor of Kirkby Ireleth.
        Consideration: £89 4s.
        Annual rent: 2s 6d and 1s in lieu of Great tythes, corn tythe rent, and half a Boon Plow.
        Witnesses: John Robinson, John Jopson.
        [Original in Prospect Estate papers].

144   *Conveyance*, 13 February 1783.   1783
        1. Roger Parker of Soutergate, Kirkby Ireleth, co. Lancaster, yeoman.
        2. John Pearson of Egremont, co. Cumberland, hatmaker.
        Premises: land at Cockfish Hall commonly known as The Meadow or The Meadows and the Browhead (boundaries given).
        Consideration: £121 15s.
        Annual rent: 2s 10d and 1s 2d in lieu of tythe.
        Witnesses: John Robinson, John Jopson.
        [Original in Prospect Estate papers].

145   *Mortgage*, 13 February 1783 (cancelled).   1783
        1. Samuel Knight of Cockfish Hall, Kirkby Ireleth, co. Lancaster, yeoman.
        2. Richard Dickinson, Kirkby Ireleth, waller, and John Lowther of Hagg, co. Lancaster, husbandman.
        Premises: messuage and tenement at Cockfish Hall and the Marshfield and the Two Newfields (boundaries noted), 2 dales in a close called Quickwoods, 1 dale in Soutergate Town Field containing 1 dale called Hampland.
        Consideration: £160.
        Witnesses: John Robinson, John Jopson.
        [Original in deeds of Prospect Estate BSUD/D].

146   *Lease*, 19 June 1783.   1783
        1. Lord John Cavendish, lord of the manor of Kirkby Ireleth, co. Lancaster.
        2. John Woodburne of Wellhouse in the manor of Kirkby Ireleth, slate merchant.
        Premises: messuage near Cockfish Hall commonly called Nanny Parke House with garden below, granary adjoining the Gateway and Willyhouse, close called Hall

Meadowhead and the 'two stewstakers' and Little Meadow (boundaries given).

Term: 1 year.

Reservation of timber, manorial rights, royalties etc.

Witnesses: J. Saunders, Anthony Hillam.

Seal.

147   *Enfranchisement* (by lease and release), 20 June 1783.   1783

1. Lord John Cavendish, lord of the manor of Kirkby Ireleth, co. Lancaster.
2. John Pearson of Egremont, co. Cumberland, hatmaker.

Premises: 3 parcels of land near Cockfish Hall near the manor of Kirkby Ireleth, i.e. meadow with occupation road running through it; meadowside with occupation road, and Browhead with housteads on it.

Consideration: £12 15s.

Fine: 2s 10d.

Obligation to grind corn, grain and malt at Grizebeck and Beckside Mills.

Reservations of oak and timber rights, of hawking, fishing, fowling, mines, minerals, metals, coals, slate and stone quarries etc.

Release of 2 to 1 of future repairs etc. of land.

Consideration: 5s.

Endorsement: memo and receipt of £12 15s.

Witnesses: J. Saunders, Anthony Hillam.

Seal.

148   *Release*, 25 December 1783.   1783

1. John Woodburne of Wellhouse, Kirkby Ireleth, co. Lancaster, slate merchant.
2. John Pearson of Egremont, co. Cumberland, hatmaker.

Premises: land at Cockfish Hall commonly called Willeyhouse (boundaries noted) and close called the Filmun.

Reservation of rights for mines, minerals, quarries and to the custom of the manor.

Consideration: £68 5s.

Witnesses: William Sherwin, Thomas Pearson.

[Original in Prospect Estate collection BSUD/D].

149A   *Notice* of a Public Sale by Samuel Nelson of Broughton in   1784

Furness, co. Lancaster, yeoman.

Premises: tenement at Sandside in Kirkby Ireleth, co. Lancaster, 24 September 1784.

[Original in Prospect Estate papers, BSUD/D].

149B   *Letter* to Lord John Cavendish from John Robinson,   1784
steward to the manor of Kirkby Ireleth, about building a
school within the manor of Kirkby Ireleth.

150   *Enfeoffment*, 7 February 1785.   1785
1. Samuel Nelson of Lancaster, yeoman, grandson and
heir of Thomas Nelson of Sandside, Kirkby Ireleth.
2. John Pearson of Egremont, co. Cumberland,
gentleman.
Premises: tenement commonly called The Bottom, or The
Bottoms, near Cockfish Hall, Kirkby Ireleth (bounda-
ries noted).
Consideration: £35.
Annual rent: 3d for corn tythe.
Witnesses: Anne Nelson, J. Postlethwaite.
Seal.
[Original in Prospect Estate papers BSUD/D].

151   *Will* of William Coward of Grofacragg, Ulverston, co.   1785
Lancaster, husbandman, made 14 October 1785.
Bequests include:
– James, son, estate at or near Grofacrag,
– William, son, clock and chest and £80,
– Ann and Jane, daughters, £60 each.
Witnesses: William Geldart, Jane Geldart.

152   *Rules and Orders to be observed by a Friendly Society and the*   1788
inhabitants of the parish of Lamplugh and its neighbourhood
(Whitehaven 1788) [16 pages].

153   *Conveyance*, 7 February 1789.   1789
1. Thomas McKnight of Cockfish Hall, Kirkby Ireleth,
co. Lancaster, waller.
2. Rev. Thomas Pearson, minster of the parish of Kirkby
Ireleth.
Premises: tenement at Quickwoods Close near Cockfish
Hall.
Consideration: £128.
Annual rent: 2s 6d and half a Boon Plow and 1s for corn
tythe in lieu of Great Tythes.
Witnesses: W[illia]m Sherwin, John Taylor.
[Original in Prospect Estate papers BSUD/D].

154   *Conveyance*, 14 February 1789.   1789
1. Samuel McKnight of Cockfish Hall, Kirkby Ireleth,
co. Lancaster, husbandman.
2. John Dickinson of Wellhouse of Broughton, yeoman,
eldest son of Thomas Dick, waller, deceased.
3. Rev. Thomas Pearson, minister of Kirkby Ireleth.

Premises: messuage and tenement at Cockfish Hall, 2 dales in a close called Quickwoods and Marshfield and High Orchard (boundaries noted).

Recital of mortgage: 13 February 1783 between 1 and Thomas Dickinson.

Consideration: £64 to 2, 5 shillings to 2 by 3, £64 to 1.

Annual rent: 1s 7¼d.

Corn tythe rent: 5d.

1 day law Boon Shering.

Seal.

Witnesses: John Mayson, George Kellett.

155   *Admittance*, 21 July 1789, by William Burnthwaite, gent.,   1789 deputy steward of the manor court of Kirkby Ireleth (held for Lord John Cavendish, lord of the manor) held at Beckside of Rev. Thomas Pearson.

Premises: a close of ground called Quickwoods with appurts. at or near Cockfish Hall of yearly rent 2s 6d.

Fine: £2 10s.

156   *Confirmation* of Conveyance, 9 October 1789.   1789

1. John Dickinson of Wellhouse in Broughton-in-Furness, Kirkby Ireleth, co. Lancaster, yeoman.

2. Samuel Knite of Cockfish Hall, Kirkby Ireleth, husbandman.

Premises: messuage and tenement at Cockfish Hall and Angerton Moss.

Confirmation of previous conveyance, 16 June 1767 between 1 and 2 and right to title.

Consideration: 5s.

Seal.

Recital of conveyance, 16 June 1767 between 1) Thomas Dickinson and 2) Samuel Knite.

Consideration: £180.

Premises: messuage and tenement with appurts. at Cockfish Hall, Kirkby Ireleth and land at Angerton Moss (except 3 dales in Mossmeadow and 1 in the Cornfield called Crosspool).

Customary rent: 5s 7d to the Lord of the Manor, 1s 6d to Rector of Kirkby Ireleth for corn tyth and 12s 6d to Lord of premises at Angerton Moss.

Admittance of Court Baron of Manor of Kirkby Ireleth of Samuel Knite as tenant of said customary messuage and tenement at Cockfish Hall.

Seal.

157   *Conveyance*, 10 October 1789.   1789
        1.   Samuel Knite of Cockfish Hall, Kirkby Ireleth, co. Lancaster, yeoman.
        2.   Rev. Thomas Pearson of Beckside, Kirkby Ireleth, clerk.
        Premises: tenement commonly called The Marshfield (boundaries given) and ground called the High Orchard and two dales in Quickwoods at Cockfish Hall.
        Consideration: £64.
        Witnesses: James Brade, John Parker.
        [Original in Prospect Estate papers BSUD/D].
        Customary rent: 1s 1¼d and 1 day law boon shearing p.a.; 5d for corn tythes.

158   *Will* of Stephen Pennington of Millhouse, Broughton, co.   1790
        Lancaster, house carpenter, made 1 June 1790. Bequests include:
        – Mary Bristow (daughter of Christopher Bristow), £2,
        – John Bristow, nephew, 1 pair of bedsteads, 1 long oak table and a box with rings, 1 dressing table,
        – Elizabeth Bristow (wife of John), bedclothes,
        – Ann, grand-daughter (wife of John Jardin, 1 feather bed and bolster and 1 blanket.
        Witnesses: Joseph Gunson, Joseph Taylor.

159   *Admittance*, 1 June 1790, by John Robinson, gent., deputy   1790
        steward of the manor court of Kirkby Ireleth (held for Lord John Cavendish, lord of the manor) held at Beckside, of Rev. Thomas Pearson, clerk.
        Premises: tenement called The Marshfield, The High Orchard and Two Dales called Quickwoods at Cockfish Hall.
        Annual rent: 1s 7¾d.
        Fine: £1 12s.
        [Original in deeds of Prospect Estate BSUD/D].

160   Feoffment, 12 February 1791.   1791
        1.   John Woodburne of Crogline, Kirkby Ireleth, gentleman.
        2.   Isaac Gillbanks of Beckside, Kirkby Ireleth, blacksmith.
        Premises: 2 dales of arable lands in Soutergate Town Field known by names of Long Dale and Knepster Road (boundaries noted).
        Annual modus: 8d in lieu of tithe on corn and grain.
        Consideration: £70.
        Witnesses: William Sherwin, John Shepherd.
        Seal.

161	*Letter*, 16 October 1791, from John Robinson, gent., to Lord John Cavendish concerning 2 deeds of enfranchisement to be executed, and of the building of a house on the last remaining tenement not yet enfranchised. (with 4 transcripts).	1791
162	*Letter*, 3 September 1792, from John Robinson, gent., to Lord John Cavendish concerning the destruction by fire of Low Barn.	1792
163	*Letter*, 1 October 1792, from John Robinson, gent., to Lord John Cavendish concerning the rebuilding of the Low Barn, and the possible opening of more slate quarries on the estate.	1792
164	*Land Tax Bill* for Kirkby Ireleth, 1792.	1792
165	*Account* of the expenses of repairing the Low Barn in 1792 and 1793.	1792/ 93
166	*Lease*, 15 January 1793.	1793

1. Lord John Cavendish, Lord of the manor of Kirkby Ireleth, co. Lancaster.
2. Rev. Thomas Pearson of Beckside, of Kirkby Manor, clerk.

Premises: ground at Cockfish Hall called Quick Woods, the March field, the High Orchard and 2 dales. Reservation to 1 of timber, seigniary, royalty and manorial rights.
Term: 1 year.
Consideration: 5s.
Seal.

167	*Letter*, 4 April 1793, from John Robinson, gent., to Lord John Cavendish concerning sale of woods on enfranchised estates and of the enlarging of the slate quarries.	1793
168	*Letter*, 13 January 1794, from John Robinson to Lord John Cavendish concerning the slate quarries and building of a house.	1794
169	*Letter*, 10 February 1794, from John Robinson to Lord John Cavendish, concerning the intended tax on slate.	1794
170	*Letter*, 3 March 1794, from John Robinson to Lord John Cavendish about the slate quarries.	1794
171	*Letter*, 21 February 1794, from John Robinson to Lord John Cavendish about the slate quarries.	1794
172	*Letter*, 24 May 1794, from John Robinson to Lord John Cavendish concerning overdue bonds.	1794
173	*Letter*, 27 June 1794, from John Robinson to Lord John Cavendish concerning repairs to the church in Kirkby Ireleth (with transcript).	1794

174	*Letter*, 26 October 1792, from John Robinson to Lord John Cavendish, concerning change of rent for tenants.	1792
175	*Letter*, 14 January 1793, from John Robinson to Lord John Cavendish, explaining accounts for the year 1792.	1793
176	*Letter*, 4 February 1795, from Thomas Riggs to Lord John Cavendish about the slate quarries.	1795
177	*Letter*, 6 February 1795, from John Robinson to Lord John Cavendish about the slate quarries, and a new wheel for a water mill.	
178	*Letter*, 14 March 1795, from John Robinson to Lord John Cavendish concerning rents and slate.	1795
179	*Letter*, 30 June 1795, from Thomas Riggs to Lord John Cavendish concerning the tax on slate and a copy of a letter from Lord George Cavendish on slate tax.	1795
180	*Letter*, 25 December 1795, from John Robinson to Lord John Cavendish about slate tax.	1795
181	*Letter*, 16 January 1796, from John Robinson to Lord John Cavendish concerning Low Barn.	1796
182	*Letter*, 20 December 1796, from Thomas Riggs to Lord John Cavendish about the slate tax.	1796
183	*Will* of John Bradley of Craggfield, Kirkby Ireleth, co. Lancaster, yeoman, made 15 March 1796. Bequests include:	

183 (continued)

- Thomas Woodburn, brother in law
- Edward Coward

    messuage, tenement etc at Craggfield for the use of Agnes, wife, during her lifetime

	– Agnes Bradley, grand-daughter, £50 from the above land to be sold on attaining her majority,	1796
	– George, son, £8 yearly.	
184	*Admittance*, 17 August 1799, by John Robinson, gent., steward of the manor court of Kirkby Ireleth (held for Lord John Cavendish) held at Beckside, of Roger Staunton.	1799

Premises: half a messuage, tenement etc at Soutergate in the said manor.

Annual rent: 5s 11d.

Fine: £5 18s 4d.

185	*Land Tax Return Form*, 1 May 1800, for John Newby, Kirkby, Ireleth, co. Lancaster.	1800
186	*Letter* to William Pitt from the proprietors and owners of the slate quarries in High Furness concerning the reduction in trade in the county of Lancaster after the tax on slate.	

187   Atkinson, Isaac, *Atkinson's Tide Table: Showing the (mean)*   1807
        times of High Water, and Heights of the Tides at Liverpool
        with the times of Crossing Lancaster and Ulverston Sands
        (Ulverston, 1807) [9 pages].

188   Front covers (9) of *Dialogue Between two intimate friends on*   *c.*1810
        Regeneration; or the New Birth (Ulverston) with text,
        originally printed by Religious Tract Society, London.

189   *Address of the Reformers of Fawdon to their brothers the*   1819
        Pitmen, keelmen and other labourers on the Tyne and Wear
        (Newcastle upon Tyne, 1819), [reprinted 1969].

190   Valuation of Estates in Kirkby belonging to Lord G.H.   1826
        Cavendish by P. Simpson, T. Bulber, J. Bispham (15
        pages), 1826, (14 page written report).

191   *Lease and Release*, 3 and 4 March 1826.   1826
        1.   Isaac Gillbanks of Beckside, Kirkby Ireleth, co. Lan-
        caster, blacksmith.
        2.   William Gillbanks of Reading, Colton, co. Lancaster,
        husbandman.
        Premises: 2 dales, the Long Dale and Knepster Rood in
        Soutergate Town Field (boundaries given).
        Consideration: £160.
        Witness: Roger Ray.
        Seals (2).
        [Original in Prospect Estate papers BSUD/D].

192   *Release*, 27 May 1826.   1826
        1.   Isabella Gillbanks of Beckside, Kirkby Ireleth, co.
        Lancaster, widow, and relict of Isaac Gillbanks.
        2.   William Gillbanks of Reading, Coulton, co. Lancas-
        ter, husbandman.
        Premises: The Dower in Dales in Soutergate Town Field
        (boundaries noted).
        Consideration: £16 12s.
        Witnesses: Joseph Gillbanks, Samuel Tyson.
        [Original in Prospect Estate papers BSUD/D].

193   *Conditions for Sale*, 22 December 1828, by auction by John   1828
        Danson of Cross, Millom, co. Cumberland, and Eliza-
        beth, his wife, at the house of James Shepherd at Askew
        Gate, Kirkby Ireleth, co. Lancaster.
        Sale of freehold messuage and tenement at Meerbeck,
        Kirkby Ireleth, either together or in lots stated.
        Witness: William Kendall.

194   *Agreement*, 23 February 1829.   1829
        1.   John Danson, the younger of Hotborrow in Millom.
        2.   George Riley of Stank in Low Furness, husbandman.

Premises: messuage, tenement at Mearbeck, Kirkby Ireleth, co. Lancaster, purchased from Elizabeth Danson, mother of 1 for sum of £370. £90 of purchase money paid for 1 by 2. 1 agrees that 2 giving security shall, at the expense of 2, vest in him the said premises, securing the repayment of the remaining part of the purchase – £280, within 12 months.
Witnesses: James Park, William Kendall.

195   *Mortgage*, 12 June 1829.   1829
1.   George Riley, servant in husbandry (son of Samuel Riley of Meerbeck, Kirkby Ireleth, co. Lancaster, farmer.
2.   John Danson of Hotborrow, Millom, co. Cumberland, farmer.
Premises: messuage, tenement in the Townfield of Kirkby Ireleth.
Consideration: £280.

196   *Mortgage*, 12 June 1829.   1829
1.   John Danson of Cross, Millom, co. Cumberland, and Elizabeth Danson, wife.
2.   Margaret Hall of Cartmel, co. Lancaster, spinster.
3.   George Riley, servant in husbandry, son of Samuel Riley of Mier Beck, Kirkby Ireleth, co. Lancaster, farmer.
4.   Thomas Butler of Dalton-in-Furness, co. Lancaster.
Premises: messuage at Mearbeck from 1 to 3.
Consideration: £370.
Witnesses: James Park, William Kendall.

197   *Land Tax Assessment* for Kirkby Ireleth parish, 1832.   1832
198   *Copy Will* of the Rev. Thomas Pearson of Kirkby Ireleth,   1832
co. Lancaster, clerk, made 28 March 1832. Bequests include:
– William Kirkby Pearson, son, estate and land, occupied by James Dodgson, and all goods, furniture, personal estate etc.
– Elizabeth Jane Pearson (daughter of John Pearson), grand-daughter, £150,
– Jane Postlethwaite, daughter, £150,
– Ann Chamley, daughter, £150,
– Isabella Pearson, daughter, £150,
– Maria Pearson, daughter, £150.

199   *Probate* of the Will of Thomas Bird of Gill Beck, Kirkby   1834
Ireleth, co. Lancaster, yeoman, 5 March 1834. Bequests include:

- William Wayles of Doveford, friend, yeoman
- William Wilson of Doveford, yeoman customary
real and personal estate at Gill Beck for the use of Sarah
  Bird, wife and thereafter to Sarah Woodend, daughter,
  and then to be given to Thomas Woodend, grandson,
- John Woodend, grandson, messuage etc at Gillbeck.
Witnesses: W. Postlethwaite, George Shepherd and
George Postlethwaite.

200   *Proof* of a will of Thomas Bird of Gillbeck, Kirkby Ireleth,   1835
co. Lancaster, 17 September 1835, admitted before Rev
Charles Robert Graham, surrogate.

201   Application for right to customary messuage and close of   1836
land called Meadow, of annual rent 6d, by Isaac Coul-
ton, before the Court Baron of the manor of Kirkby
Ireleth belonging to William Earl of Burlington, at the
schoolhouse at Beckside, 31 May 1836. Signed Thomas
Butler, Steward.

202   *Release*, 5 March 1844.   1844
1.   James Gillbanks of Four Lane Ends, Kirkby Ireleth,
co. Lancaster, labourer.
2.   William Kirkby Pearson of Whitehaven, co. Cum-
berland, draper.
Premises: 2 dales (formerly called Long Dale and Knepster
Rood) in Soutergate.
Consideration: £140.
Witnesses: Thomas Postlethwaite.
[Original in Prospect Estate papers BSUD/D].

203   *Release*, 5 March 1846.   1846
1.   James Gillbanks of Fourlane Ends, Kirkby Ireleth, co.
Lancaster, labourer.
2.   William Kirkby Pearson of Whitehaven, co. Cum-
berland, draper.
Premises: two dales (formerly called Long Dale and
Knepster Rood) in Soutergate, Kirkby Ireleth.
Consideration: £140.
Recital of Will of Joseph Gillbanks late of Beckside,
Kirkby Ireleth, 25 April 1835. Bequests include:
- Joseph (deceased) and James Gillbanks, nephews,
  messuage in Kirkby Ireleth and real estate with proviso
  that Ann Gillbanks, wife may occupy the said premises
  rent free or let farm and receive rents during her natural
  life.
Witnesses: Thomas Postlethwaite.
Seal.

204   *Receipt*, 5 March 1846, for £10 by James Gillbanks from   1846
William Kirkby Pearson of Whitehaven, co. Cum-
berland, draper, paid for the sale of Moss on Angerton
Moss, Kirkby Ireleth, co. Lancaster (boundaries noted).

205   *Admittance*, 9 June 1868 by William Butler, steward of the   1868
manor court of Kirkby Ireleth (held for William, Duke
of Devonshire) held at Stone Arthur, of George Coulton
and Joseph Coulton.
Premises: 1 messuage with appurts'. at Soutergate within
the said manor.
Annual rent: 6d.
Fine: 10s.

206   Kirkby family tree taken from Sir William Dugdale, *The*   1872
Visitation of the County Palatine of Lancaster: made in the
year 1644–5, edited by Rev. F.R. Raines (Chetham
Society 1872).

207   *Mortgage*, 13 February 1875.   1875
1.   George Riley of Ireleth, co. Lancaster, labourer.
2.   John Knowles of Ireleth, butcher, and William
Knowles of Ireleth, labourer.
Premises: 2 cottages with land and farm buildings, called
Mere Beck Farm, Kirkby Ireleth, co. Lancaster.
Term: 6 years.
Rent: £27 per annum.

208   *Prints* (2) of 'Crossing the Sands', *c*.1877.   *c*.1877

209   *Assignment* of a Lease for £1000, 23 March 1878.   1878
1.   Joseph Ward of Storey Square in Barrow-in-Furness,
co. Lancaster, cabinet maker.
2.   George Riley of Kirkby Ireleth, co. Lancaster, shoe-
maker, and John Riley.
Premises: messuage and tenement, at or near Meerbeck,
Kirkby Ireleth and land in the Town Field called the
Guards. Rights of winterage.
Consideration: £100.
Witness: George S. Goddard.

210   *Surrender* of Lease by Endorsement, 8 November 1878.   1878
1.   John and William Knowles of Ireleth, co. Lancaster.
2.   John Riley of Wallsend, near Broughton-in-Furness,
co. Lancaster, farm servant.
Premises: 2 cottages with land called Mere Beck Farm,
Kirkby Ireleth, co. Lancaster.
(With accompanying letter).

211   *Conveyance*, 13 December 1878.   1878
1.   George Riley of Ireleth, co. Lancaster, shoemaker and

John Riley of Wallsend near Broughton-in-Furness, co. Lancaster, farm servant.
2. William Cloudsdale of Dunnerholm Gates, Dalton-in-Furness, co. Lancaster, husbandman.
Premises: messuage and tenement at and near Merebeck, Kirkby Ireleth, co. Lancaster; land called High Croft and Low Croft and land in the Town Field called The Guards. Rights of winterage in other closes.
Witness: U.J. Hardy.

212   More, Hannah, *The Shepherd of Salisbury Plain* (Ulverston   1883
       1818) 32 [reprinted by Religious Tract Society 1883].

213   *Notice of sale* by Auction of Ashlack Hall, Kirkby Ireleth,   1886
       co. Lancaster, 27 August 1886, with plan and particulars
       of the estate.

214   Extract from *The Coucher Book of Furness Abbey*, printed   1886–
       by the Chetham Society, edited by Rev. J.C. Atkinson,   1887
       3 parts (1886–7).

215   *Will* of Edward Hall of Dalton-in-Furness, co. Lancaster,   1890
       surgeon made 11 October 1890. Bequests include:
       – Mrs. Dyer, relative, of Winchelsea, £50,
       – Mrs. Stone of Deptford (daughter of Mrs Dyer), £50,
       – James Atkinson of the Rookery, Ulverston, £200,
       – Mary Ann Atkinson and Hannah Atkinson, daughters of
       his late niece Hannah, £500 each,
       – Arthur Cross, assistant, £50,
       – Catherine, Deborah and John Atkinson, servants £20
       each,
       – children of Hannah Johnson £2500 between them at the
       age of 21.
       Witnesses: William Taylor, Cha[rle]s H. Thomas.
       Codicils (4) – 1 April 1891; 15 June 1891; 29 April 1892;
       22 July 1892.

216   Petty, S.L., '"Grounds" in Furness and Cartmel'; *The*   1900–
       North Lonsdale Magazine and Furness Miscellany, edited   1902
       by Rev. L.R. Ayre, (June 1900–August 1902) IV, 260.

217   Pages (2) from *Millom Auction Mart Co. Year Book* relating   1902
       to sale at Kirkby Hall.

218   *Table* of Soutergate Marsh owners, 26 October 1902.   1902

219   *Report* on Endowed Charities to the County of Lancaster: 1903
       Subsection for Kirkby-in-Furness and the extra paro-
       chial place of Angerton (H.M.S.O. 1903). 3 pages.

220   Cowper, H.S., 'The Kirkbys of Kirkby-in-Furness, in   1905
       the Seventeenth Century illustrated by their Portraits',
       Transactions of the Cumberland and Westmorland

	Antiquarian and Archaeological Society, N.S. (1905) VI, 97–127.	
221	Gaythorpe, Harper, 'A Bishop's Visitation to Furness in 1554', *Transactions of the Cumberland and Westmorland Antiquarian and Archaeological Society*, N.S. (1907) VII, 273.	
222	Endowed Charities: Return, [Hundreds of Amounderness, Lonsdale (North of the Sands) and Lonsdale (South of the Sands) and County boroughs of Barrow-in-Furness and Preston], (London, 1908) I, 245–267.	1908
223	*Evening Gazette* 'Heart of The Fylde', 25 October 1930.	1930
224	*Evening Gazette* 'The Golden Heart of the Fylde', 27 June 1931, with accompanying letter 6 June 1970 from Chief Librarian of Blackpool Central Public Library.	1931
225	*Questionnaire*, 8 November 1952, on dialect use of words relating to forms.	1952
226	*Yorkshire Observer Budget*, 6 March 1953, article in dialect 'bi Buxom Betty'.	1953
227	*Yorkshire Observer Budget*, 8 May 1953, article in dialect 'bi Buxom Betty'.	1953
228	D'Angerville, Howard Horace, Count, *Living Descendants of Blood Royal (in America)*, compiled by A. Adams, (London and Paris, 1959), IV 532–35.	1959
229	*Barrow News*, 'Kirkby Literary Society: Kirkby folk enjoy flip into history', 16 January 1959.	1959
230	Girouard, Mark, 'Burrow Hall, Lancashire', *Country Life*, 14 April, 21 April 1960, parts 1 and 2.	1960
231	*Script* with accompanying letter for B.B.C. T.V. production of 'Benbow was his name', 10 August 1965.	1965
232	*Application form* to, and reply from, Parcel Office at Liverpool by E. Fieldhouse concerning loss of mail to J.L. Kirby, 27 January, 2 April 1966.	1966
233	Genealogical tree of General Washington and typed sheet of descent of Kirby family showing their connection with Washington and ultimately Charlemagne, 1 January 1967.	1967
234	'Letters to the Editor', *The Field*, concerning a previous article on Lord Wakefield of Kendal, 13 April 1967.	1967
235	Danvers-Walker, Bob., 'The Vikings land at Peel', *In Britain*, No. 7, (July 1967), XXII 5, 27–9.	1967
236	'The Furness Railway' by Maureen [Richardson] of Barrow-in-Furness with accompanying letter, 28 August 1967, (48 pages, student thesis).	1967
237	*List* of field names and acreages belonging to Ashlack Hall.	1968

238	*Pamphlet* on coal mining.	1969
239	Haigh, Christopher, *The Last Days of the Lancashire Monastries and the Pilgrimage of Grace* (Manchester 1969), 2 extracts.	1969
240	Lewis, B.M. and Kirby, L., *The Wiggs of Beaufort District, South Carolina*, 136–43.	1971
241	*The South Carolina Historical Magazine*, no. 2 (April 1971), LXXII, 129 comprising a list of recent publications.	1971
242	Editorial comment in the *New York Times* of obituary to Allan P. Kirkby, 3 May 1973, and other newspaper biographies (5 pages).	1973
243	*Map* of Lancashire boundaries for 1974 Government Reorganisation.	*c.*1974
244	Standard letter from the Minnisink Oil Company Inc., to American citizens concerning reduced consumption of petroleum fuel.	1974
245	*Article* 'British budget to soak rich, help the poor', *The Star Ledger*, (27 March 1974).	1974
246	*Article* 'Time to let Enoch Powell Save Britain', *The Review of The News* (3 April 1974), 31–40.	1974
247	Article about the possible sale of the Achnabourin Estate in Strath Naver with plan of the house *The Field* (1 August 1974).	1974
248	*List* of records deposited in Dalton Library from Dalton U.D.C. offices, 23 April 1975.	1975
249	*Brochure* of 'Wakefield-in-the-James', Virginia, with accompanying letter, 8 October 1975.	1975
250	Short biography of J.L. Kirby by Loretta L. Lombardo dated 11 January (8 pages).	*c.*1977
251	Currer-Briggs, Noel, *'Thomas Kirby of New Poquoson – some notes on early settlers in York County and Elizabeth City, Virginia*.	n.d.
252	Currer-Briggs, Noel, *Similarity of Surnames in York County, Virginia, and County Norfolk, England*, n.d. 5 pp.	n.d.
253	*Cumbria* 'Herdwick Tips for Hire' [Eskdale Show].	n.d.
254	*Extract* from magazine article on Gainsborough's portrait of John Joshua Kirkby and his wife, n.d.	n.d.
255	Grundy, Bill, *'The Counties of Britain: Lancashire'*, vol. 49, 2 pages.	n.d.
256	Hodgson, Joseph, 'Verses on The Extraordinary Trial of Dr. William Palmer' [Whitehaven Library].	n.d.
257	Kirby family – genealogical tree of 16–17th century branches including links with the names of Copley,	n.d.

	Kinge, Kirby, Rolston, Wormeley, Chicheley, Wray, Bosville and others.	
258	Kirkby Manor – typescript of boundaries.	n.d.
259	Kirkby, Roger, of Kirkby Hall – inventory (with transcription).	n.d.
260	Knipe, Walter, Dixon, 'Fleeackin at Fleeachbarra' – a story written in dialect (4 pages).	n.d.
261	'Mumming' from *Yorkshire Dialect Society Journal* pp. 13–16.	n.d.
262	Rolfe, Wilfred, E., 'The Counties of Britain: Buckinghamshire', vol. 13, pp. 32–38.	n.d.
263	Entry from Tithe Award Book for George Riley of Kirkby Ireleth.	n.d.
264	*Inventory* of estate and particulars of William Wayles of Kellet Ground, Kirkby Ireleth.	n.d.
265	Wills and Inventories in *The Archdeaconry of Richmond*, including a transcript of the will of Anne Kirkbie, 12 September 1566.	n.d.
266	Rhyme about Thomas Woodend of Kirkby, written on a page of a printed book containing 'Didactic Pieces,' 19th century. (Another copy: Fieldhouse Scrapbook No. 11., p. 86., *c.*1853).	n.d.

BD/F 6

6/1–25 Scrapbooks 1–25

This is the most important section of the collection. The scrapbooks are of uneven size and design; beside each page, the entry gives the subjects of the cuttings, but their scale and detailed format may vary considerably.

6/1	*Scrapbook 1*	
Doc. 1.	Typed account of election procedure in Cumberland, 1806.	1806
Doc. 2.	Typed account of canvassing in Westmorland 1818.	1818
Doc. 3.	Letter, 30 October 1963, re the customs of the Manor of Kirkby-in-Furness from R.B. Charles, The Holker Estate Office, Cark-in-Cartmel, Lancs. (ph).	1963
Doc. 4.	Extract regarding Furness place names from *Domesday Geography of Northern England*, H.C. Darby and J.S. Maxwell (London, 1962).	1962
Doc. 5.	Letter, 1 October 1958 re the Plea Rolls from Duchy of Lancaster Office, The Strand.	1958

(BD/F 6)

Doc. 6.	Letter, 15 October 1958 from Public Record Office, Chancery Lane, re references to Kirkby Ireleth in Duchy of Lancaster records.	1958
Doc. 7.	Duchy of Lancaster Ancient Deeds. Extracts from *The Coucher Book of Furness Abbey*, 5 pages (Manchester 1887) printed for Chetham Society.	1887

6/2   *Scrapbook 2*

1st division

pp 1–7   Kirkby Ireleth Parish and all the regions within it; name derivation of each division etc. (article).

2nd division

pp 8–13	'Kirkby Ireleth parish' from P. Mannex *Topography and Directory of North and South Lonsdale* (1886) 416–27 (ph).	1886

3rd division

pp 14–17	The Burlington Schools: article.	
p 18	'Opening of the Burlington Schools, Kirkby', *Barrow Times* (April 1878).	1878
p 19	The Burlington School Log Book 1878–1879, extract.	1878–1879
p 20	'Opening of the Burlington School', newspaper report, second part (ph).	
p 22	Newspaper report re loss of sheep in Kirkby storm, and 3 old women at Sandside, extract.	
p 23	Unpolished jet beads by the Dickinsons of Soutergate House, article.	
pp 24–27	'Real Whitby Jet' from *Cassell's Family Magazine* (1882) 143–46.	1882
p 28	'Victorian Jet Set' by Donald Wintersgill, *Guardian*.	
p 29	'Little Wonder Washer', advertisement (1882).	1882
pp 30–32	*The Farm and the Household*, extract (ph).	
p 33	Stephenson's 'Locomotion', drawing from *The Guardian* 31 October 1974.	1974
pp 34–35	'The Story of George Stephenson' article.	
pp 36–38	Extract from *Early Railway History in Furness* by J. Melville and J.L. Hobbs (Kendal, 1951), originally published in the *Transactions of Cumberland and Westmorland Antiquarian and Archaeological Society*, no. 13 (ph).	

49

	Household recipes, Goodall.	1883
	Johnston's Corn Flour.	1884
	McCall's Ox Tongues.	1885
p 3	Poulton & Noel's Belgravian Tongues.	
	Dulcemona Tea.	1897
	Brown & Polson's Corn Flour.	1870
	Fry's Cocoa.	
	Frederick Mason's Home Made Beef Tea.	
	Nestle's Milk Food.	1885
	Cooper Cooper & Co. Tea.	1885
p 4	Dr. Ridge's Patent Food for Infants and Invalids.	1883
	Nestle's Milk Food.	1884
	Pears Soap.	1884
	Hubbard's Scotch Rusks.	
	Borwick's Baking Powder.	1885
	John Richard Wace & Co. List of Wines.	1870
	'Kerlio' from Madame S. Argent.	
p 5	Pear's Soap.	1884
	Dr. De Jongh's Light Brown Cod Liver Oil.	1883
p 6	Godfrey's extract of Elder Flowers.	1870
	Cuticura Remedies.	1894
	Bailey's patent rubber 'complexion' brush and washing glove.	1894
	Beecham's pills.	
p 7	Pear's soap.	
	Pear's Shaving Soap.	
p 8	Vaseline	1885
	Pear's Soap.	1884
p 9	Guy's Tonic.	
	Jewsbury and Brown's Oriental Tooth Paste.	
	Kaye's Worsdell's Pills.	1894
	White's Belts.	1894
	Eno's Fruit Salt.	1883
p 10	Browne's Chlorodyne.	
	Rowlands Kalydor.	1870
	Perry Davis' Pain Killer.	
	Owbridge's Lung Tonic.	
	Digestive Lentil Flour.	
p 11	Pear's Soap.	1883
	Pear's Soap.	
p 12	Holloway's Ointment.	
	Eno's Fruit Salt.	1884
	Kirkby's Patent Miniature Dispensaries.	1870
	Glycerine and Honey Jelly.	1884
	Murray and Lanman's Florida Water.	1894

p 13	Calvert's Carbolic Tooth Powder.	1900
	Price's Regina Soap.	1898
	Bile Beans.	
p 14	G.T. Congreve *Consumption*.	
	Rowland and Sons Pears Dentifrice.	1870
	Kearsley's Widow Welch's Female Pills.	1870
	Perry Davis' Vegetable Pain Killer.	
	Osler's China and Glass Services.	1883
p 15	Foot's Drawer Trunks.	1897
	Orchestral Organette.	1894
	The Autophone from Campbell & Co., Glasgow.	1885
	C. Churchill and Co., *Household Elegancies*.	1883
	Heal and Sons's Bedsteads etc.	1884
	The Abingdon Card Squares.	1899
	New Harrison Knitter.	1896
	Lincolnshire Feather Beds.	1885
p 16	Hitching's Baby Carriages.	1884
	Tate's Patent Travelling Trunks.	
	Cooper and Holt, cabinet makers and upholsterers.	1870
	Adam's Furniature Polish.	
	Goodhall, Backhouse & Co., *Good Things*.	1884
	Venables' American Organs.	1885
	Bartholomews' Furniture and Carpets.	1870
p 17	Fitch's Patent Fire Wheels.	1870
	J. Adam's Furniture Polish.	
p 18	Judkins' Sewing Machines.	1870
	The Alberta Lock-stitch Family Sewing Machine.	1870
	Harris & Co. Defence Lock-Stitch Sewing Machine.	1899
	Singer Sewing Machines.	1870
p 19	Grover and Baker's Sewing Machines.	1870
	Triumph Dress Fastener.	
	Walpole Brothers' Irish Linens.	1894
	Weir's Sewing Machine.	1877
	Cash's Woven Names.	
	Theobald & Co: British Sewing Machines.	1894
	Lion Embroidery Trimmings.	1895
	W.J. Harris & Co.'s Defiance Lockstitch Sewing Machine.	
	Weir's Sewing Machine.	1870
	Singer Sewing Machine.	1870
p 20	R. Slinger and Son Saw Makers.	1882
	Goddard's Plate Powder.	
	Price's Gold Medal Palmitine Candles.	1884
	Hebden's Silver Gloss for Linen.	
	James' Gold Medal Dome Black Lead.	1884
p 21	Wright and Butler's Cooking Stoves.	1884

	Entwistle & Kenyon Wringer and Mangles.	1885
	'Handy' Knife Cleaner.	1897
	Hauthaway's Peerless Gloss for blacking and polishing.	1894
	Wright's Eureka Gas Cooker.	1884
	The 'Vowel' Washing Machine.	1870
p 22	Staffordshire China.	1894
	William Whiteley Ltd., China Dept. of Bayswater, London	1900
	Staffordshire China by Hassall & Co.	1897
p 23	Atkinson's Silk Poplins.	1884
	Crewel Silk.	1894
	Alexander's Sewing Cotton.	1884
	Baldwin and Walker's Knitting Wools.	1884
	Carr's Patent Woven Tapes.	1883
	Cash's Cambric Frillings.	1885
	Frilled Butter Muslin.	
	Baldwin and Walker's Knitting Wools.	
	Paton's Alloa Wools.	
p 24	Rosenthal's Patent Postulata Corset.	1883
	Arthor Puckett & Co. fitters.	
	Allison's 'Argyll' Corset.	1894
	W. Thomas, The 'Duchess' Corset.	
	The Y and N Diagonal Seam Corset.	1884
p 25	The 'Rational' Corset Bodice.	1899
	The Lovely Figure Configurateur of Bale and Co.	
	The Y and N Diagonal Seam Corset.	1899
	The Oktis Corset Shields.	
	The Y and N Diagonal Seam Corset.	1883
	Dr. Warner's Coraline Corsets.	1894
p 26	Allen Foster 'The Alfosco Costumes'.	1899
	Macclesfield Silks.	1899
	The John Noble Costumes.	1899
	McCallum's Kals.	1898
	John Piggott collars and cuffs.	1885
p 27	John Piggott 'Argosy Braces'.	1883
	The London Glove Company: Gloves and Hosiery.	1900
	The John Noble Costumes.	1897
	The London Glove Company.	1897
	Allen Foster costumes.	
p 28	Egerton Burnett's Royal Serges.	1885
	The Tudor House Association Boy's Overcoats.	1894
	The Ladies' Shopping Guides.	1894
p 29	Straw Hat Reviver.	1900
	J. Theobald & Co.'s Specialities.	

	Ladies' Waterproof Cloaks.	1884
	Cambric Pocket Handkerchiefs.	1884
	Mary Harrison, *The Skilful Cook: a practical manual of modern experience* (London 1884).	
	Royal National Life-Boat Institution: Services.	1884
p 30	The Distingue Waterproof.	
	Lane's Baby Linen.	1884
	Vorwerk's Shirt and Dress-Band.	
	Harrod's Stores' Boys Clothing and Outfitting Dept.	1894
p 31	Steel's Beau Ideal Seamless Umbrella.	1884
	The 'Parker' Umbrella.	1884
	Accordian Dresses for Dancing.	
	Etanche Serge of Jolly & Son., Bath.	1886
	Lahmann's Cottonwool Combinations.	1895
	Egerton Burnett's Royal Serges.	
	Ladies 'Scarboro' Costumes.	1884
	Small & Son 'The Knicker-Skirt'.	
	Crawshaw's Crystal Dyes.	1894
	The Couldthorp Direct Trading Concern.	1894
p 32	Macniven & Cameron's New Pens.	
	Philips' Large Penny Coloured Maps.	
	Goodhall, Backhouse & Co. Leeds 'Household Recipes'.	1883
	Mudie's Select Library.	1870
	Girls and Boys' Own Paper.	1885
p 33	Hughes' Physical and Political Maps.	
	'The Cottager and Artisan', magazine for working people.	1884
	Macniven & Cameron's The Big Waveley Pen.	1883
	The Graphic, illustrated weekly newspaper.	1870
p 34	'Announcements for the Season', 1881–2.	1881–
	'Educational works of Dr. Cornwell'.	1870
	Charles Dickens, *The Mystery of Edwin Drood* (1870).	1870
	The Religious Tract Society: *Half Yearly Volume The Cottage & Artisan Volume.*	1870
p 35	S.O. Beeton's Books and Serials.	1870
	The Child's Companion and Juvenile Instructor, by Religious Tract Society.	1884
p 36	Four Popular Volumes.	1884
	Joseph Gillott's Steel Pens.	
	The Religious Tract Society – coloured diagrams and pictures.	1883
	The Boys, Girls Own Paper.	1884
	The Psychic Research Co. *The Power Within.*	
	Shilling Books for Working People.	1883
p 37	Norman MacLeod, ed., *Good Words.*	

6/7   *Scrapbook 7*

p 1   Letters about scrapbooks from 'Ellie' of Beckside, October   1974
1974.

Opening of the Burlington Schools, Kirkby-in-Furness and   1876
entertainments provided by the Duke of Devonshire 8
March (1876) (ph).

p 2   The assassination of Lord Frederick Cavendish, second son   1882
of the Duke of Devonshire on 6 May 1882 in Dublin
(article) (ph).

Entertainments on the opening of Burlington Schools,
Kirkby, article (ph).

p 3   A race between 2 men at Elliscales, article.
A large goose egg at Leece, near Barrow, article.
Quakers meeting house at Swarthmoor, article.
Letter by Lady Frederick Cavendish after death of husband.
Dinner at the Stamford Hotel for R.N.
Todd-Newcomb with friends and tenants from Kirkby,
article (ph).

p 4   Anniversary of the 'Church of Christ' at Ulverston (ph).
Opening of a new meeting house in Kirkby Ireleth (ph).

p 5   Obituary of William MacDougall at Kirkby Ireleth.
'A Tattooed Man and a Spotted Boy', article.' 'Spring' and
'The Poor hard Working Boy', poems.
'Statue of Robert Raikes unveiled on Victoria Embankment'
and 'Sunday School Children gather at Lambeth Palace',
articles (ph).

p 6   'Lines to a Skull' and 'Late Snowdrops', poems.
John Knox, article.
'The Great Gathering at a Grand Soiree'.
James Carter's Funeral, North End Prison, Port Elizabeth
(poem).

p 7   '3 English sea-captains and others see Mr. Booty of Wop-   1876
ping and another fly into Stromboli volcano', [14
December 1876].

Funeral of J.L. Stubbs of Shifnal [14 December]   1876
Three poems.
Kirkby Friendly Society, advertisement.
140 year old man, article (ph).

p 8   Ulverston preacher keen on Whiskey, article.
Parish of Lodge-on-the-Wolds sent to prison.
Discovery of Royal Mummies in Egypt, taken to Boulak
Museum.
Wall End Sunday School Anniversary.
Death of S.R. Bigg of Ulverston.

'A Mother's Care' and 'All for the Best', poems.

Attitudes to wine over the centuries, article (ph).

p 9 The Bright family who own the Rochdale Mills.

Story of Thomas Fell, c.1310.

Funeral of J. Livesey at Preston.

'Christmas 1884', 'General Gordon', 'In Memoriam', poems.

Boy George Barr drowns in Kirkby Pool.

Archaeological discovery of a city near Mobeley, Missouri (ph).

p 10 'Lament of Thomas', and 'The Messenger', poems.

Will of Nathaniel Caine, including estate at Broughton-in-Furness.

Article about late Mrs. King, daughter of Robert Walker of Gargreave, Kirkby.

Death of Joseph Postlethwaite of Kirkby Ireleth.

Death of Hannah Nelson at Sandside, Kirkby Ireleth.

Medal for George Burrent of Middlesex.

Joseph Cartmel of Kirkby gives a Bible and Prayer Book from Sunday School (ph).

p 11 Elections for the Fylde Union – Freckleton.

Ulverston Union – Upper Allithwaite,

Aldingham, Urswick,

Kirkby Ireleth,

West Broughton,

Rural Districts.

600 sheep lost at Kirkby-in-Furness. Poem 'Old Kirkby'.

Triple birth at Kirkby Ireleth.

John Gunson of Oak Bank, Ulpha, Cumberland; will bequests.

The First Poetry written in America (ph).

p 12 'Lines to a brother' and 'It Doesn't cost money', poems.

3 ladies at Sandside.

A poor student in Vienna.

Mr. Gordon Smith's performing otter.

Meeting of workmen at Burlington Slate Quarries, Kirkby Ireleth on death of Lord Frederick Cavendish.

'Via Solitaria', poem (ph).

p 13 Letter concerning infant baptism, 21 March 1876.   1876

Death of Dr. De Vitre of The Elms, Bare, near Lancaster.   1876

'Polemics at Coniston', 21 March 1876.

Death of Joseph Jackson of High Torver Park, aged 88.

Death of Rev. Matheson, aged 90 at Patterdale, Westmorland.

Re-building of the Beckside Sunday School, Kirkby.

p 14	Death of Isabella, wife of Jeremiah Bussey, daughter of William Parker, Soutergate, Kirkby Ireleth, died 2 September 1874.	1874
	Marriage John Walton Ainscough, draper, to Betsy, second daughter of E. Johnson of Kirkby Ireleth.	
	Marriage of Alex Brownlee to Mary Postlethwaite of Kirkby Ireleth.	
	Marriage of James Parkinson of Blackburn to Rebecca Alice, youngest daughter of George Mason, Ashlack Hall, Broughton-in-Furness, 29 May 1878.	1878
	Death of Agnes, wife of John Hindson, and daughter of Thomas Casson of Knittleton, aged 39 years, 4 July 1878.	1878
	Marriage of William Rigg to Jane Benson of Kirkby Ireleth, 26 June 1880.	1880
	Marriage of William Myers to Sarah Knight of Kirkby Ireleth, 26 June 1880.	1880
	Marriage of Richard Thompson of Ulverston to Frances Mary Wood of Lindal, 26 June 1880.	1880
	Death of Thomas Postlethwaite, aged 45 years, 17 July.	1880
	Obituary of John Sawrey of Broughton Tower, Lord of the Manor of Broughton.	
	Death of James Barr of Kirkby Ireleth.	
	Obituary and death of Rev. G. Pickering of Holy Trinity Church, Ulverston.	
	Barrow Naturalists' Field Club Literary and Scientific Association excursion to Silverdale.	
	Inscription in Coniston Church to Alice Fleming of Coniston Hall, eldest daughter of Roger Kirkby of Kirkby.	
	Article on Church of England Temperance Society in Whitehaven (ph).	
p 15	'Lean Upon My Arm, Mother'; 'A Message for Mamma in Heaven'; 'The Silver Lining'; 'Not Always'; 'A Mother's Love'; 'Jessie's Growing'; 'My Mother's Grave', poems.	
	Kirkby Ireleth Parish Magazine: Article on parish registers April 1892 (ph).	1892
p 16	Mrs. Margaret Rigg, wife of Thomas Rigg, right leg amputated, October 1853.	1853
	Description of the proceedings on the day of the opening of the Burlington Schools at Kirkby Ireleth. Songs noted, speech by Lord Edward Cavendish, and speech by Sir James Ramsden.	1853
	Mr. Thomas Teague of Birmingham, insane, article.	
	Religious article quoting from the scriptures (ph).	
p 17	Annie Chapman, Whitechapel victim (Jack the Ripper), short story.	

H.M. Stanley, article.
'Misunderstood', poem.
'Wedding in Westminster Abbey between Mr. Stanley and Dorothy Tennant', article.
Obituary – Susan Wilson died 28 May in 91st year.

p 18   Articles on courtship and proposals.
List of bones found during excavation near Bleaberry Haws, Torver.
Meeting of Liberals in the Schoolroom, Ireleth.
Letter on the Kendall family.
Kendall property in Chancery.
Rev. Hagemore of Catshoge, Leicestershire, died 1 January 1776, article.
Betty Craughwell, 101 years, article.
Tyson Family of around Kirkby Ireleth, article.

p 19   'For the Young A New Years' Gift'; 'For an Invalid', 'Childrens' Evening Hymn', poems.
'Giant found at St. Bees (folklore), article.
James Heard, Native of Egremont who emigrated to America early 19th century, article.
Funeral of John Brown (ph).

p 20   Tips for house and garden.
Kirkby Cooperative Society Jubilee – Committee for the Sports (ph).

p 21	Kirkby Ireleth Parish Magazine – March, June, July, October.	1892
	Kirkby Ireleth Church Monthly, April, September, December 1893, January, April, June 1894.	1893– 1894
p 22	Kirkby Ireleth Parish Magazine – February, September.	1888
p 23	Kirkby Ireleth Parish Magazine – January 1890, November 1889.	1889– 1890
p 24–26	Kirkby Ireleth Parish Magazines, February, March, May, June, October, November.	1890
p 27–29	Kirkby Ireleth Parish Magazines, February, March, April, May, August, September, 1891.	1891
p 30	List of burials for August 1896, and programme for Kirkby Ireleth parish Children's Concern.	1896
	List of baptisms, burials, church services and choir account for the year, September 1896.	1896
p 31	Baptisms, marriages, burials, for May 1897, and account of Easter celebrations.	1897
	Baptism, marriage, burial and account of help for the deaf and dumb, the Carlisle Victoria Clergy Pension Fund, and the celebration of the Queen's Jubilee at Kirkby Ireleth – July 1897.	1897

p 32	Lists of baptisms, marriages, burials and church services for Kirkby Ireleth, January 1898.	1898
	Lists of baptisms, marriages, burials, confirmation, Church Army Cottage Meetings and Services, February 1899.	1899
	Back cover: list of baptisms, marriages, burials, cottage meetings, for December 1899.	1899
	Loose papers – Kirkby Ireleth parish magazine for December 1892.	1892
6/8	*Scrapbook 8*	
	Illustrations from old magazines of childrens' stories 1875–85 (32 pages).	1875–1885
6/9	*Scrapbook 9*	
	Extracts from copies of magazine *London Society*, collected by a subscriber from Soutergate House, Kirkby-in-Furness, January 1885–December 1885.	1885
6/10	*Scrapbook 10*	
	Cassell's Family Magazine April 1881; advertisements.	1881
	The Woman at Home, 1900–1906; extracts.	1900–1906
6/11	*Scrapbook 11*	
	Front cover – Barrow Chrysanthemum Society, 7 November 1953, Third prize ticket.	1953
	Card with halfpenny on it.	
p 1	Introductory page.	
p 2	Transcription of undated newspaper cutting concerning the manorial court of Mr. Victor C.W. Cavendish.	
p 3	The parish boundaries of Kirkby Ireleth.	
p 4	1898 Newspaper cutting on aspects of Kirkby.	1898
	'Christmas decorations at the Kirkby Church' from *Ulverston News*, 28 December 1895.	1895
	'Charities and the Children's Concert at Kirkby', *Ulverston News*, 28 December 1895.	1895
	Lowden and Postlethwaite, auctioneers, advertisement.	
p 5	Kirkby Church Magazine January 1903.	1903
p 6	Postcards: The Punch Bowl Inn, Old Railway Station, Kirkby-in-Furness, and four scenes of Kirkby in one postcard.	
p 7	Kirkby Church Magazine for September 1909.	1909
	Old Kirk newspaper photograph.	
p 8	Article on Kirkby, 17 September 1903.	1903

	Kirkby Horticultural Society, 19 June 1903, article.	1903
	Advertisement for freehold estates for sale.	
p 9	Letters from Joan Parsons of Leeds, re Newton of Soutergate.	
p 11	'Kirkby Ireleth Band of Hope', entertainment for 6 April 1878, advertisement.	1878
p 12	Programme of children's entertainment at Grizebeck Board Schools, 21 December 1892.	1892
p 13	Advertisement for readings at the Burlington Slate Works, 20 November 1869.	1869
	Postcard: Burlington Slate Quarry.	
p 14	Old postcards (3) of the workers at Burlington Slate Quarries, 21 March 1904.	1904
p 15	'Scholars of Burlington School, Kirkby', c.1897 from *The News*, 24 June 1950.	1950
p 16	Photograph of Kirkby children at the local Cooperative Jubilee in 1911 from *The News*, 16 February 1968.	1968
	Postcard of Slate Quarry, Kirkby.	
p 17	Newspaper cuttings (5) about Kirkby, January 1901, April 1902, 11 December 1902, 9 May 1904.	1901–1904
p 18	Kirkby Horticultural Society, 18 December 1902.	1902
	'Rejoicings at Kirkby', 11 December 1902.	1902
p 19	Newspaper cuttings about Kirkby: 10 September 1 October, 8 October, 6 October, 29 October and November 1904.	1904
p 20	Newspaper cuttings about Kirkby, April 1905, 1904, 5 December 1908.	1904–1908
p 21	Coronation of George V celebrations at Kirkby, pamphlet.	
p 22	Programme for Kirkby and Broughton Choral Group Concert for 10 April 1947.	1947
p 23	'Forget-me-not' card.	
	Envelope dated 1877 to Miss Fleming, Sandside, Kirkby, Carnforth.	1877
	'The Widow of Kirkby', story.	
p 24	'The Widow of Kirkby' continued.	
	Certificate of the 'Band of Hope' for Mary Jane Sykes.	
	Golden Wedding invitation from W. Postlethwaite and Mary J. Sykes of Glen Cragg, Kirkby-in-Furness.	
	Golden Wedding Card: Thomas Newby and Elizabeth Mary Rigg (1886–1936) of Low Mere Beck, Kirkby-in-Furness.	1936
p 25	Church of Christ, Wallend, two photographs.	
p 26	Reminiscences of Richard Tyson, aged 74, in 1941, of Kirkby-in-Furness.	1941

	Newspaper articles of Kirkby and a Festival at Marshside given by Mrs. William Postlethwaite of 'Glen Crag', Kirkby.	
p 27	Cumbrian form of numerals for counting sheep: source Mr. H. Mason, Littlecroft, Kirkby-in-Furness.	
p 28	Postcard of Herschell Terrace, Kirkby-in-Furness.	
	Postcard: after the fire at Kirkby Cooperative.	1969
	Reminiscences by Mrs. M.G. Wills, 27 April 1969 about the Society 'Band of Hope'.	
p 29	Reminiscences of large circle above High Ghyll House, called the 'Kirk', and names used on 'April Fool's Day', and Easter mummers' play.	
p 30	Newspaper cuttings for Kirkby, 10 October 1914, 2 January 1915 and 21 April 1916.	1914–1916
	Photograph of Edwardian gentleman.	
p 31	Newspaper cuttings for Kirkby: 16 March 1920 Football; Band of Hope, Dramatic Society; 1929 Cricket Club and Church of Christ; poem 'The Broken Hearted' by Alex E. Jenkin of Mavisbank, Kirkby.	1920–1929
	Postcard: Kirkby Cricket Club.	
p 32	Marshside Chapel, 3 postcards.	
	Kirkby Ireleth 'Band of Hope' photograph.	
p 33	Kirkby Ireleth Church Magazine, May 1921.	1921
	Typed extract from parish letter, December 1958.	1958
p 34	Guide to St. Cuthbert's Church, Kirkby Ireleth, 1924.	1924
p 35	The death of Reverend G.W. Sykes, Vicar of Kirkby Ireleth, 1929, 3 newspaper cuttings.	1929
p 36	*The News*, 5 January 1929, 29 November 1913, 30 March 1929, 14 February 1953, news about Kirkby.	1913–1958
p 37	Gill House Beck (including the Kirk). 4 photographs supplied by Barrow Field Naturalists (1963).	1963
p 40	Tennis court in Kirkby, playing Miss Pennington, Mr. J. Cartmel, Mrs. C. Cartmel, Mr. T. Barr, photograph.	
	3 August 1912 – A football team, postcard.	1912
p 41	Kirkby Hall, 2 photographs.	
p 42	Kirkby Hall in 1895 (magazine), Kirkby Hall Old Door, Kirkby Hall the 'Long' table, photographs.	
p 43	Newfield Hotel, Seathwaite, and Proprietor, 25 July 1904. (postcard).	1904
	Vicar and the cricket team, 14 July 1913, postcard.	1913
	'Going up the Incline', postcard.	
p 44	Mrs. Dickenson of Soutergate House cuts the cake for the Festival of Britain, 1951, photograph.	1951
	3 boys in grounds of Kirkby Hall, photograph.	

Old Kirkby, photograph.
'In Memoriam' cards for Charles Harrison 1863–85,
Isabella Helling Lings 1864–1919; James Postlethwaite
1837–1905.

p 45   Wedding photograph of Miss Adelaide Hester Machell of   1926
Ulverston, and Dr. Walter Graham Southern of
Broughton, 16 October 1926, *The Guardian.*
Photograph of Kirkby.
Old saying of Jane Wilson, aged 78.
Three letters, 30 January 1969 from J. Neville, 6 February   1969
1969 from Ellie, and about Tithe Barn, Pinfold Pad-
dock, The Burts.

p 46   Printed letter from the Vicar.
Article about two sisters in a village, 26 February 1971,   1971
The News.

p 47   How to play the game 'Spell and Knur' by John Bart.
p 48   Article on foods in Furness.
p 49   Miss J. Hall Johnson of Prospect House, Kirkby Ireleth,
newspaper photograph.
Chrysanthemums owned by John Bell of Kirkby Ireleth,
newspaper photograph.

p 50   Photographs (10) of the Fieldhouses and others, 1934–47.   1934–
1947
p 51   Accounts for month of October 1939 from A. Fieldhouse   1939
to J. Cartmell, joiner and builder.

p 52   List of words used in Dialect Society.
Letter from Isabella Cartmel, 19 July 1969.   1969
The Guardian, 23 January 1969 'Few now known thrang
maudiwarp'.
Will of James Cartmell, article.

p 53   Calendar of Kirkby Ireleth Coronation Festivities.
p 54   Programme for St. Cuthbert's Players presentation of 'The   1954
Babes in the Wood', February 25–27, 1954.

p 55   The Three Shire Stones (boundary of Kirkby Ireleth
parish), magazine photograph.
Duddon Estuary from Kirkby, postcard.
Kirkby Post Office, postcard.
Visit of Cumberland and Westmorland Antiquarian and   1966
Archaeological Society and Barrow Field Club around
Ulverston and Grizebeck, May 1966, article.

p 56   Snow at Kirkby in 1940, photographs (7).   1940.
p 57   'Kirkby 60 to 80 years ago' by Matthew Stables (ph),   1938
Barrow News, 10 December 1938 (ph).

p 58   Obituary for Matthew Stables of Greenhow, Kirkby
Ireleth.

	The Mill, Kirkby-in-Furness, postcard.	
	'Farm Service' by Matthew Stables, poem.	
p 59	Toast Card of the Kirkby Ireleth Literary Society, 30 April 1953.	1953
	Syllabus, September – December 1946 Kirkby Ireleth Literary Society.	1946
p 60	Syllabus, January – March 1949 Kirkby Ireleth Literary Society.	1947
	Kirkby Ireleth Literary Society, speech for 1953.	1953
p 61	International One-Act Play Theatre, 22 April 1952, receipt.	1952
	Licence to perform a play from Samuel French Ltd., London, 22 April 1952.	1952
p 62	Programme for four plays – The Neighbours by Yves Cabrol, First Corinthians by H.F. Rubinstein, The Happy Journey by Thornton Wilder, Sometimes in October by B. Douglas Arnot, performed by Kirkby Ireleth Drama Group.	
p 63	Letter from Clerk of the North Lonsdale R.D.C. concerning the Rights of Way Map for Kirkby Ireleth Parish, 3 March 1967.	1967
p 64	The Vicarage, St. Cuthbert's Church, and Quarry Incline in Kirkby Ireleth, postcards.	
p 65	Programme for Kirkby-in-Furness Flower Show.	1950
	First prize certificate for Kirkby and District Floral and Horticultural Society, 1947.	1947
	Second prize certificate for Kirkby and District Floral and Horticultural Society, 1948.	1948
p 66	The Drama Class 1954 at Kirkby, 5 photographs.	1954
p 67	Script for 'John Winder', by Edmund Casson.	1956
p 68	Amang T' Roundheeads poem.	
p 69	'Our Village', by Mrs. Coulton, poem.	1957
p 70	'The Bidden Wedding' by John Hales-Tooke.	
	'Local custom of barring out the schoolmaster'.	
p 71	The Church Treasures, Kirkby Ireleth.	
p 72	Interior of Church, 1957; Lettering cut in stone; Kirkby Fell from the 'Beck Lane', photographs.	1957
p 73	Kirkby Ireleth Literary Society Christmas Party, 1953, 7 photographs.	1953
p 74	Medieval cock fighting, drawing.	
p 75	Roger Kirkby by James S. Dearden, *Evening Mail*, 25 June 1965 (ph).	1965
	Restored portrait of Roger Kirkby, 1603.	
p 76	Edward Rigby (1603) and Roger Kirkby (1603) on wall of 'Crestley' Morristown, now owned by J.L. Kirby; Arms	

	granted to J.L. Kirby by College of Heralds 1967; Roger Kirkby sitting on a chair made by a Kirkby carpenter (*c*.1890), photographs.	
p 77	Beckside and Askewgate by R. Vere, screenprints.	1953
p 78	The Old Mill, Kirkby-in-Furness, postcard.	
	The Old Mill, photograph.	
p 79	'Parish Magazine gives glimpse of life in Kirkby 52 years ago', *Barrow News*, 27 January 1961.	1961
	Article on sledges by E. Williams, Halton, Lancaster (ph).	
p 80	Kirkby Literary Society, article (ph).	
p 81	'The fascinating story of Kirkby-in-Furness' by Ellen Fieldhouse, *Barrow News*, 29 May 1959 (ph).	1959
p 82	'Kirkby heirlooms show life as our Forefathers knew it' *Barrow News*, 27 March 1959 (ph).	1959
p 83	'Kirkby – England's largest Slate Quarry – sparks off a new era', *Barrow News*, 21 January 1966 (ph).	1966
p 84	Furness Railway engines, 1923, newspaper photograph.	1923
	The new railway steamboat docks at Barrow, opened September 1867, magazine photograph.	
p 85	The Old Pack Bridge, Kirkby Ireleth, photograph. The Church, Kirkby-in-Furness, postcard.	
p 86	'Road danger in Kirkby-in-Furness', *The News*, 14 November 1975.	1975
	Writing in a school book, 1853 (ph).	1853
p 87	'The Villagers, welfare organisation and social activities of Kirkby', *The News*, 1 February 1963 (ph).	
p 88	Kirkby W.I., *The News*, 22 July 1965.	1965
p 89	'A Pre-medieval Secret in Kirkby Hall Attics', *Barrow News*, 2 March 1962 (ph).	1962
p 90	'Biggest sale of antique silver since pre-war days', *The News*, 8 June 1962 (ph).	1962
	Two horses, postcard.	
p 91	Meeting of the Cumberland and Westmorland Antiquarian and Archaeological Society at Kirkby Ireleth, 14 May 1966, programme.	1966
p 92	Letter from the President of the Cumberland and Westmorland Antiquarian and Archaeological Society, 16 May 1966.	1966
	Letter from the excursions secretary of the Cumberland and Westmorland Antiquarian and Archaeological Society, 11 June 1966.	
p 93	Kirkby Art Show, 25 March, in Beckside Hall, newspaper photograph.	
p 94	List of painters who exhibited at the art show.	

p 95	Kirkby W.I. – photograph.	
p 96	Kirkby-in-Furness 1964, photograph.	1964
	Kirkby-in-Furness over 60's, 25 April 1969, newspaper photograph.	1969
p 97	British Legion Christmas Party, newspaper photograph.	1968
p 98	Tithe Redemption Communion – Tithe Act 1936 Redemption Annuities, 30 September 1942.	1942
	Back cover : Bookmarks (2).	1931
	Carving of names under the floor of Beckside School in 1931 (ph).	
6/12	*Scrapbook 12*	
	Front cover: 'Swillmakers, enquiries into Kirkby family, and the old custom of Merrie Neet', article.	
p 1	'Kirkby folk enjoy flip into history', 5 January 1959.	1959
	'Kirkby People in Canada', *Barrow News*, 16 February 1959.	1959
p 2	Letter from Richard A. Parsons about Kirkby Literary Society, 18 January 1959.	1959
	Letter from R. Strike, editor of the *Barrow News*, re her article 'Kirkby Night', 19 January 1959.	1959
p 3	Letter from Carr's Flour Mills Ltd. re an order of Oat-flour, 30 December 1958.	1958
	Cartoon of a 'cultured cottage'.	
p 4	The *Parish Magazine* 1959, with advertisement for Burlington Slate Quarries, S.J. Curwen (baker), G. & E. Benson (engineers), W.A. McAtee (embalmber), cuttings.	1959
p 5	The *Parish Magazine* for baptisms, marriages and burials for the year 1959, cuttings.	1959
p 6	Photograph showing skaters on Derwent Water; weather in the Lake District; article on Windermere frozen, *Manchester Guardian*, 10 February 1959.	1959
p 7	Review of J.D. Marshall's *Furness and the Industrial Revolution*, *Manchester Guardian*, 10 February 1959.	1959
	Parish Magazine, February 1959 – article on The Guides.	1959
	'Boundary Commission to make no changes?', *Barrow News*, 20 February 1959.	1959
p 8	'Some amusing customs and superstitions', report on Kirkby Ireleth Literary Society talk, 20 February 1959 (ph).	1959
	'Pantomime by St. Cuthbert's Players' in Beckside School, *Barrow News*, 13 February 1959.	1959
	Local Furness tradition of eating cheese, *Cumbria*, February 1959.	1959

p 9	'£71,250 road plan will begin soon: Improvements near Kirkby', *Barrow News*, 13 February 1959.	1959
	Mrs. Mary Woodend, British Legion Poppy Day organiser for Kirkby-in-Furness area, *The News*, 10 April 1959, article.	1959
	'Lime-spraying planes crash near Broughton', *Barrow News*, 29 May 1959.	1959
p 10–11	'Kirkby heirlooms show life as our forefathers knew it', *The News*, 27 March 1959.	1959
	'Association for the prosecution of felons' in Kirkby area, *North Western Evening Mail*, 23 June 1961.	1961
p 12	'The fascinating story of Kirkby-in-Furness', *Barrow News* 22 May 1959.	1959
	Letter in newspaper about Kirkby family.	
	Silver plate at Kirkby Church, *Cumbria* August 1961.	1961
p 13	'Parish Magazines give glimpse of life in Kirkby 52 years ago', *Barrow News*, 27 January 1961.	1961
	Article on Mrs. Egan-Newcomb in Kirkby, *Barrow News*, 3 February 1961.	1961
	Pagan worship, newspaper article.	
p 14	Hawkshead Show, *The News*, 4 September 1959.	1959
	Barrow Show, article.	
p 15	Pictures from Millom Show, *The News*, 4 September 1959.	1959
	Garden Party at Seattle, 1959, photographs.	1959
	Church magazine article on garden party.	
p 16	'Furness Folk in Exile: Mr. and Mrs. Brian Wills'; 'A brief history of the Church at Kirkby'; Literary Society's tribute to Dr. R. Parsons'; 'A Country Diary: Keswick', *The News*, 1 April 1960.	1960
p 17	'Furness Folk in Exile: Mr. Norman Grigg', *The News*, 23 September 1960.	1960
	Weather in former days, *North Western Evening Mail*, 11 January 1962.	1962
p 18	'The Kirkby and District Floral and Horticultural Society annual show,' article.	
p 19	'Lorry hits a church in crash at Grizebeck', *Barrow News*, 9 May 1961.	1961
	Crash at Grizebeck, article.	1961
	Presentation to William Satterthwaite of Kirkby, *Barrow News*.	
	List of those ordained by the Bishop of Carlisle, *Barrow News*.	
	Kirkby Ireleth parish council matters, article.	
p 20	'Pensioners' New Club at Kirkby' and 'Kirkby Mothers'	1961

Union give £5 to old people', *Barrow News*, 29 September 1961.

'Kirkby Women's Unionist Association', *Barrow News*, 9 March 1962.   1962

'A Country Diary', *The Guardian*, December 1961.   1961

'Dalton's ancient registers are now being published', *The News*, 2 February 1962.   1962

'In Bygone Days', article.

p 21   The Lake District at 50,000 ft. from Avro Vulcan bomber, *The Guardian*, 1 January 1962.   1962

Driver trapped in his lorry at Grizebeck Hill, *The News*, 2 March 1962.   1962

p 22   'Bridge over Duddon Estuary – 19th century idea', *The News*, 9 March 1962.   1962

Railway at Kirkby, *North Western Evening Mail* : 4 April 1962.   1962

'Bare settler' in a Kirkby club. *North Western Evening Mail*, 5 April 1962.   1862

'A Duddon 'Dream' Bridge can be reality', *North Western Evening Mail*, 28 February 1962.   1962

p 23   'A pre-medieval secret in Kirkby Hall attics', *The News*, 2 March 1962.   1962

p 24   'A Country Diary : Westmorland', *The Guardian*, 13 April 1962.   1962

'A Country Diary : Cumberland', *The Guardian*, 22 August 1962.   1962

Two Kirkby boys found in London, article.

Two men trapped in lorry wreckage at Grizebeck, article.

p 25   'Judges' praise for cookery at Kirkby', article.   1962

'Kirkby Old People's Welfare', *Barrow News*, 23 November 1962.   1962

Vehicle out of control at Grizebeck, article.

p 26   'Lorry overturns on Grizebeck Hill', *The Guardian*, 25 July 1962.   1962

Antique sale at Little Croft, Kirkby, *The News*, 3 June 1962.   1962

Jersey Cow at Royal Lancashire Show, *The Guardian*, 1 August 1962.   1962

p 27   'A Country Diary: Westmorland', *The Guardian*, 15 February 1962.   1962

'A Country Diary: Westmorland', *The Guardian*, 8 November.

p 28   'The villagers, welfare organisations and social activities at Kirkby', *The News*, 1 February 1963.   1963

p 29	Kirkby Over 60 club, *Melrose Review*, 7 May 1964.	1964
	Grizebeck Village Hall, *Barrow News*, 11 January 1963.	1963
	'Lakelands' Own Sheep; The Hardy Herdwicks', *The News*, 8 March 1963.	1963
p 30	Gales' damage in Furness, 14 January 1965.	1965
	'3 saved by Helmets in Rock Fall Kirkby quarry accident'. North West gets a battering in gales.	
p 31	Roger Kirkby, *North West Evening Mail*, 25 June 1965.	1965
	American professor visits Kirkby, *Parish Magazine* May 1965.	1965
	New English Bible presented to Bob Marr, *Parish Magazine* May 1965.	1965
p 32	Kirkby over 60's, *Parish Magazine*, May 1965.	1965
	Kirkby over 60's, *Parish Magazine*, July 1965.	1965
	Granada T.V. features Barrow people in 'Scene at 6.30', article.	1965
p 33	Kirkby W.I. *The News*, 23 July 1965.	1965
p 34	Kirkby W.I., *Barrow News*, 11 September 1965.	1965
	Burlington Slate, advertisement.	
	Letter from the Vicar of St. Cuthbert's Church, Kirkby Ireleth, 19 July 1965.	1965
p 35	Lowick Show, September 1965, newspaper photographs.	1965
	Road accident at Grizebeck, 6 December 1965, newspaper photographs.	1965
	Kirkby Flower Show, 21 August 1965, article.	1965
p 36	Letter from Rev. E.C. Whitaker to Mr. Kirby, 9 June 1965.	1965
	Letter to Ellen Fieldhouse from Lancashire Parish Register Society, 3 May 1965.	1965
	Letter from Ellen Fieldhouse to Rev. Whitaker enclosing cheque for 5 guineas from J.L. Kirby.	
	Extract from parish magazine of gift from J.L. Kirby.	
p 37	'Coastal protection Scheme', *Barrow News*, 1 October 1965.	1965
	Programme for Sandside Gospel Hall Services, 4–18 October.	
p 38	Monthly news letter from Church of Christ, Wall End, Kirkby-in-Furness, October 1965.	1965
p 39	Crash at Grizebeck, *Evening Mail*, 19 October 1965.	1965
	'Marsh Grange has links with history', *The News*, 20 July 1962.	1962
p 40	Grizebeck Hill, *The News*, 10 and 17 December 1965, articles.	1965

p 41   Grizebeck Hill, articles, 31 December 1965, 7 January   1965–
        1966, 27 January 1966.   1966
        A Country Diary: Keswick, *Guardian*, 25 April 1966.   1966
p 42   Morecambe Bay Barrage, *The Guardian*, 17 January 1966. 1966
        Kirkby Water Mill, *The News*, 31 December 1965.   1965
p 43   Burlington Slate Quarries, *The News*, 21 January 1966. 1966
        Wildfowlers in the Duddon Estuary, *Evening Mail*, 10   1966
        February 1966.
        Wildfowlers, *Guardian*, 10 February 1966.   1966
        Parish Magazine for February 1966.   1966
p 44   'Churches and Chapels of the Duddon Valley', article.
        Back cover : Burlington Slate, advertisement.   1964
        'A Furness diarist of the 1800's', *The News*, 3 January
        1964.

6/13   *Scrapbook 13*
        Inside cover: Photograph of Ramblers' Association   1958
        crossing the sands from Hest Bank to Grange over   1967
        Sands, *Manchester Guardian*, 25 August 1958.   1967
        Furness Fells, *Guardian*, 5 June 1967.
        Dutch Agnes and her Valentine by W.G. Collinwood, curate
        at Whittlegate, extract (ph).
p 1   List of words used in School Dialect Survey.
        County Councillor S.H. Baker reading proclamation about
        the annual fair and market at Broughton-in-Furness,
        photograph, *Manchester Guardian*.
p 2   Riot and killing in Seathwaite, *The News*.
        'Herdwick Royal' at the Eskdale Show, *Cumbria*.
p 3   The spinning gallery at the Farmer's Arms, Lowick, near
        Ulverston, magazine photograph.
        The Church of Holy and Undivided Trinity, Kendal,
        drawing.
p 4   'Crafts of the Duddon Valley', *The News*, 1 October 1965.   1965
p 5   'Christmas in Lakeland', magazine letters from readers.
p 6   'Painting recalls Ulverston's Shipbuilding days', *Evening*   1967
        Mail, 11 May 1967.
p 7   Painting of the 'Bessie Whineray' ship sold at Christies for 1967
        40 guineas, *Evening Mail*, 12 May 1967.
        Roger Sawrey's Bible, article.
p 8   Letter from J. Beck to the editor of the *Lonsdale Magazine*, 1821
        July 1821, copy.
        'Livving off the land' in West Cumbria, by Elizabeth
        Birkett.

71

List of the fairs in Cumberland.

p 9   Guide to St. Cuthbert's Church, Aldingham.
Guide to St. Mary's Church and Dalton Tower, Dalton-in-Furness.

p 10   St. Mary and St. Michael Church, Urswick; The Sir John Barrow Monument, Hoad Hill, Ulverston; The Abbey of St. Mary, Furness; Conishead Priory near Ulverston, 12th C.; A drawing of country scene.

p 11   Bardsea; St. Cuthbert's Church, Aldingham; The Priory of St. Mary; and the Nuns of Gleaston Castle, drawings.

p 12   The Church of St. Margaret, Dalton-in-Furness; Church of St. Michael, Hawskhead, drawings

p 13   St. Peter's Church, Ireleth with Askam; Holker Hall, Cark in Cartmel, Lancashire; Swarthmoor Hall near Ulverston; Aldingham Hall near Ulverston, drawings.

p 14   'A Country Diary : Westmorland', *The Guardian*, 14 August 1967, article.   1967
'The Legend of Manaton Church Cross, Devon', article.

p 15   'Broughton – a township with roots deep in history', *The News*, 24 May 1963.   1963

p 16   'Byegone days in Ulverston', article.
Newspaper letter about the above.
'More Memories of byegone Ulverston', article.
'Enjoyed reading about byegone days', letter.
The Old Market Square, Ulverston, drawing.

p 17   'A Trip down Memory Lane in Urswick', *The News*, 28 April 1967.   1967

p 18   'The Charcoal burners of Backbarrow', newspaper letters.   1967
'Bygone days in the Leven Valley', *The News*, 12 May 1967.   1967

p 19   'Happy Days in Lindal of Long Ago', *The News*, 26 May 1967.   1967
'Another incident of Lindal long ago', article.

p 20   'Tour of Furness Forts', article.   1967
'Pennington and the Abbey : 400 years of dispute', *Evening Mail*, 21 July 1967.

p 21   'When Grange men were "rude and unlettered"'. *The News*, 19 May 1967.   1967

p 22   'Broughton Fair Day', newspaper photograph.   1967
'Preparing the 300 year old fish stones at Broughton', *Guardian*, August 1967.

p 23   Major M.E. Sandys reading the annual proclamation for Broughton Fair, and children looking on, *The News*, 4 August 1967, photographs.   1967

p 24	Duchy of Lancaster, article and accompanying letter to Mrs. Fieldhouse from Duchy of Lancaster Office, Lancaster Place, London WC2, 3 November 1965.	1965
p 25	'Buying up a length of old railtrack' [27 July 1965].	1965
	'Battle for Roose Station', *Evening Mail*, 26 August 1965.	1965
	Reopening of Ulverston – Lakeland railway line, August 1967.	1967
p 26	Cark Hall, near Cartmel, article.	
	Ulverston exile's memories, *Barrow News*, 25 August 1967, article.	1967
	Memories of the National School, article.	
p 27	Aerial view of Furness Abbey, newspaper photograph.	
p 28	'Hawkshead, "best kept" Village', *Guardian*, 11 August 1967.	1967
	The Old Church at Grasmere, article.	
	More Memories of Ulverston characters', article.	
	Mrs. Mary Armer and her son outside the Drunken Duck, near Hawkshead, newspaper photograph.	
p 29	'Cumberland Union Bank in Ulverston – its history', *The News*, 3 November 1967.	1967
	A Country Diary: Westmorland, article.	
	H.M.S. Resolution, Britain's first Polaris submarine, article.	
	Ticket from Kirkby-in-Furness to Barrow.	
	The Crown Hotel at Coniston by R. Jameson of Barrow, drawing.	
p 30	Cargo liners 'Prometheus' and 'Protesilaus', magazine photographs.	
	H.M.S. 'Warspite', magazine photograph.	
p 31	Cumberland and Westmorland Antiquarian and Archaeological Society at Furness, *The News*, 8 September 1967, photograph.	1967
	'Protesilaus', photograph and article.	
	'Detroit "exile" recalls farming days and folk of long ago', *The News*, 13 October 1967.	1967
	Letter on diminution of shell-fish.	
p 32	Piel Castle, article and photographs.	
p 33	Letter, 'More memories of Old Ulverston' of Mrs. E.J. Gross, Auckland, New Zealand.	
	Charcoal burners at work near Haverthwaite; newspaper photograph and letter from Mrs. J.A. Long, Rose Cottage, Newton-in-Cartmel, with two more photographs.	

p 34	'Exile remembers Dalton in "The Good Old Days"' by Kathleen A. Brown, *The News*, 10 November 1967.	1967
	'More memories of old Dalton days', article.	
p 35	Reminiscencies of Dalton by Florence Athersmith of 5 Well Lane, Ulverston.	
	Letter on trade of charcoal burning by Herbert S. Barker of Dalton.	
	'Blind Jimmie', *The News*, 17 November 1967, photograph.	1967
	Reminiscences of Dalton by Mr. B.M. Grice, 15 Stafford Street, Askam.	
p 36	Navy takes over its first Polaris submarine: H.M.S. Resolution, *The Guardian*, 3 October 1967.	1967
	'Resolution' returns from sea trials, article.	
p 37	Legend of Spanish Armada ship wrecked near Barrow in 1588, *The News*, 24 November 1967.	1967
	Staff outing from Barrow Shipyard in 1914, *The News*, 17 May 1963.	1963
p 38	Completion at Barrow of Polaris armed submarine 'Repulse', 17 May 1968.	1968
	History of Cocken Village near Furness Abbey, now disappeared, *Evening Mail*, 1 March 1968.	1968
p 39	Barrow Military Brigade Brass Band, 1913; Ulverston Amateur Operatic Society 1931; Ulverston Dale Street School pupils.	1913, 1931
	Two Furness hoteliers and a Millom exile, newspaper photographs.	
p 40	Typescript on sheep-scoring numerals and bibliography.	
6/14	*Scrapbook 14, recipes*	
p 1	Raised Meat Pie.	
p 2	Minst pie, from *The Good Hous Wives Treasurie* 1588.	
	Traditional Cumberland Raised Pie.	
p 3	Sweet pie – Hawkshead.	
	North Country Sweet pie.	
	Yorkshire spice loaf.	
	North Country Sweet Pie.	
p 4	Recipes from Rose Turner of Walney Island.	
p 5–6	Letters from Rose Turner about recipes, 16 October 1963.	
p 7	Pickled oyster cockles or mussels.	
	Lobster cutlets.	
p 8	Cooking fish for invalids.	
	Braised crab.	
p 9	Scalloped mussels.	
	Scalloped fish.	

p 10	Devilled White Bait.	
	Potted Skate.	
p 11	Samphire pickled.	
p 12	Roast Wildfowl.	
	Yeast dumplings.	
p 13	Pickled eggs.	
	Chestnuts.	
p 14	Preserve Strawberries in wine.	
	Cowslip or Dandylion wine.	
p 15	Hard ginger bread.	
	Biscuits.	
p 16	Belvidere cakes.	
	Biscuits of fruit.	
p 17	Figged soup.	
	Snow pancakes.	
p 18	Damson cheese.	
p 19	Lemon cheese.	
	Easter Ledge pudding.	
p 20	Hert Pudding,	
	Herb Pudding, 4 articles.	
p 21	The old way of making butter – from Mrs. Hugh Barton of Kirkby, 1963.	1963
p 22	Jugged Hare and Baked Ham with Flour Paste – from Mrs. Ethel Holloway, Gill End, Kirkby Ireleth, April 1966.	1966
p 23	Stewed tripe and onions.	1965
	A Country Diary: Keswick kitchen, *The Guardian*, 1 November 1965.	
p 24	Rum Butter: from Miss Mason, 1959.	1959
	Boiled fruit cake, *Barrow News*, 1970.	
	Old way of making ice-cream.	
p 25	Mead.	
p 26	Beef and Ham Roll and Potted Butter, from Ella Robinson, West View, Kirkby Ireleth.	
p 27	Gingerbread from *The Art of British Cooking* by Theadora Gibbon.	
	Recipe for the cup cake.	
p 28	Gingerbread, from E. Atkinson	1958
	Malt loaf (1958) from Mrs. Bell, Prospect Cottage.	
p 29	Broth, from Mrs. Ethel Atkinson, of Soutergate.	
p 30	Letter from Jessie Moorhouse, 26 April 1963.	1963
p 31	Wedding Cake, from Mrs. Atkinson.	
	Royal Icing, from E. Holloway, Gill End, Kirkby Ireleth.	
p 32	Rich Christmas Cake.	

p 33   Plum pudding.

p 34   Chocolate log.

p 35   Toffee (excellent), Toffee, Toffee Chocolate, Crackey
            Toffee: from Mrs. Gelderd, Ulverston.
            Old Fashioned treacle toffee.

p 36   Butter toffee.
            Treacle toffee.

p 37   Caramel toffee, from Mrs. Bowden, Sandside.
            Home made sweets by Amy Cohen (newspaper article).

p 38   Rich scones.   1970
            Quince jam from *Dalesman*, October 1970.

p 39   Oak Cake Haverbread.
            Lancashire bun loaf.
            Coconut macaroons.

p 40   Ovaltine Granny Loaf.
            Easter Cakes, from Sarah Shaw, Soutergate.

p 41   Brandy Snaps.
            Gingernuts. Tea Round the Table, *Guardian*, article.

p 42   Pilchard Crumble, *The Guardian*.
            Tea by the Fire, article.

p 43   Gingerbread men, from Miss Ella Newby of Combe
            Crescent.

p 44   Petticoat Tails, by Nell Hecton, article.
            Scotch Shortbread, from Mrs. M. Simpson of Gawthwaite
            Village.
            Grasmere Gingerbread, from Miss Mason of Littlecroft.

p 45   Shortbread.
            Fish Souffle.

p 46   Brown Snaps.
            Oat meal biscuits.
            Lemon Jumbles.
            Ginger snaps, from Miss E. Turner, Beckside. Kirkby
            Ireleth.

p 47   Puff pastry from Kirkby W.I.

p 48   Puff Pastry, from Mrs. E.J. Turner of Beckside, died
            1914.
            Bible Cake.
            Currant pastry, from Levens Hall.

p 49   Tomatoe and Apple Chutney, from Mrs. Coward.

p 50   Piccalilli, from Mrs. Jack Coward.

p 51   Rhubarb Chutney.
            Apricot Jam.
            Summer Pudding.
            Perfect Raspberry Jam.
            Redcurrant Jelly.

p 52	Rosemary Humes, from Mrs. George Campbell.
p 53–55	Ministry of Food Austerity recipes (after Second World War); Parkin biscuits; Boiled fruit cake; Plain cake; Chocolate cream icing; Fruit cake; Christmas cake; Sweet oatmeal biscuits; Ginger biscuits; Savoury biscuits; Steamed jam pudding.
p 56	Pineapple pudding, from Mrs. Sarah Shaw, Soutergate. Almond paste, from Mrs. Holloway.
p 57	Australian biscuits. Suet puddings.
p 58	Elderflower wine. Apple cider, from Mrs. J. Postlethwaite of Glen Crag.
p 59	Apple cider, from Mrs. Cartwright. Bottled fruit, from Mrs. Clark, 27 September 1943.
p 60	Elderflower wine, from A. Stephens. Blackberry wine, from A. Stephens.
p 61	Seed cake, from Mrs. A. Bowden, Sandside, Kirkby Ireleth.
p 62	Home made bread and tea cake, from Mrs. Burns, Sandside.
p 63	Handwritten article on 'Killing a pig', by Mrs. Hugh Barton formerly of Gill End Farm.
p 64	Black pudding, from Mrs. Hugh Barton. What's in a black pudding, *The Guardian*.
p 65	Cumberland sausage, from Mrs. Hugh Barton. Poultry dressing.
p 66	Old English Cider Cake, from Mrs. G. Gardiner of Skill Hill Farm, Kirkby Ireleth. Home measures.
p 67	Recipes with blackberries: Blackberry cream; Blackberry wafer pie; Blackberry cheese; Baked Blackberry pudding; spiced Blackberries, *The Guardian*, 12 August 1966. 1966
p 68	Stuffings from Mrs. George Campbell (Winne Dickinson). Chestnut stuffing; sausage-meat stuffing; forcemeat balls' bread sauce; sage and onion – Goose; oatmeal stuffing.
p 69	'Where the Cookie Crumbles', by Skeffington Ardron. Parkin.
p 70	Marmalade, from Mrs. George Campbell. Marrow jam.
p 71	Sweet sauces; Apricot sauce; Banana sauce; Black treacle sauce; Quick caramel sauce; Cherry sauce; Cider sauce; Ginger sauce.
p 72	Cumberland Tatie Pot, *Cumbria*.

	Mulled Ale.	
	Rhum Butter.	
	Dried herbs.	
p 73–74	Herbs: Bay, Baln, Basil, Borage, Chervile, Chives, Conander, Fennel, Garlic, Horse Radish, Marjoram, Mist, Parsley, Rosemary, Sage, Savoury, Tarragon, Thyme.	
p 75	Chocolate cake from Jill Wills.	
p 76	Bird's Custard powder; Bovril; Victorian advertisements.	
p 77	Flummery: 'to make a Veal Glew'; to make Flummery; Whipped Syllabub; 14thC salad; a pie of Umbles; Lockets' Raspberries.	
p 78	Chocolate Caramel, October 1968.	1968
p 79	'Cooking with Quinces', by Ambrose Heath.	1933
	Shortbread, from Miss E.S. Whyte (Walney), 1933.	
	'Hill Top Diary', *The News*, 13 December 1968.	1968
p 80	Cream of cauliflower soup.	
	Apple and Almond flan.	
	Pot Roast.	
	The Housekeeper's Alphabet.	
	Cold meat mould, *The News*, April 1971.	1971
p 81	Rose Hip Syrup, from Joan Chapman.	1968
p 82	To preserve eggs, from Mrs. Buskby, Ulverston, 6 December 1968.	1968
	'Teatime Treats' by Winifred Barrand: Cheese cakes, Devonshire splits; Oatmeal scones; Honey nut rolls; Scotch Whiskey cake; Pineapple cake; Brandy snaps.	
p 83	Wassailing mugs, *Cumbria*, May 1970.	1970
	Letter, 4 August 1970 from K. Harrison enclosing recipes for winemaking: 5 gallon Bitter Beer; Dandelion wine.	1970
	1 gallon Cumberland Brandy; Parsley wine (1 gallon); 5 gallon strong dark ale; sherry; orange wine.	
p 84	'A Superb Red Wine', Rhubarb wine; Canadian Whiskey; Mock Tokay; Rosehip and Fig.	
p 85	Simnel cake.	
	Marmalade, from Jane Wilson, 20 February 1975.	1975
	'Wassail bowls'; Cumberland Rum Butter; Cumberland sauce, *Cumbria*, January 1975.	
	'New Ways with fruit', by Winifred Barrand.	
p 86	Baked Cranberry pudding.	
	Basic Cranberry preserve.	
	Pear Campote in red wine.	
	Damson cheese.	
	Blackberry Kissel.	
	Caramel Tart.	
	Caramelled Grapes.	

p 76	Queen of Puddings. Sponge flans. Magdala Pancake. Apple upside-down. Mousses. Bread and butter.	
p 88	'Simnel Cake and its connection with Mothering Sunday', _The News_, 6 March 1970.	1970
p 89	Gingerbread Men. Simnel cake. Clipping time pudding. Tonics for illness.	
p 90	Rum Butter, '_Cumbria_'.	
p 91	Orange Drizzle Cake, from Wesley Thompson, 26 June 1970. Coconut Ice, Chocolate Crunchies.	1970
p 92	Oatmeal biscuits from Wesley Thompson, 26 June 1970. Scotch eggs, July 1971, from Jill Wills.	1970
p 93	Fairy Cake, from Jill Wills, 8 November 1970.	1970
p 94	List of specialities in various counties – Northumberland, Durham, Cumberland, Westmorland, Lancashire, Isle of Mann, Yorkshire, Derbyshire, Cheshire and Staf- fordshire, from _The Observer_.	
p 95	Coffee Walnut Gateau; Bilberry Flan a la Mode; Pineapple Marshmallow; Melon Ginger Ice; Raspberry Meringue Glace; Apricot Whip; Mocha Sundae; Tipsy Cherry Sundae; Toffee; Orange Rum; Golden Almond; Cho- colate Fudge. Oatbread, from _The Journal of the Yorkshire Dialect Society_.	
p 96	Sweet Butter, from _The Journal of Lakeland Dialect Society_, Christmas 1971.	1971
p 97	Mrs. Beeton article with recipes, Onion Soup, Turbot a la creme, stewed Shin of beef.	
p 98	Herbs and Spices chart.	
p 99	'The Good Housekeeping Kitchen Chart for Busy Cooks'. Loose leaf: Biscuit Cake; Article 'baking with yeast'. Back cover: 'Butter toffee' from Jackie Wills, Easter 1978.	1978
6/15	_Scrapbook 15_ Inside cover: 'Cleveland Lyke-Wake Dirge', poem.	
p 1	Letter from Ellen Fieldhouse to Mr. Franks, headmaster about school dialect test.	
p 2	Letter from J.T. Franks of Dowdales Country Secondary School, Dalton-in-Furness enclosing scripts in reply to above letter.	

p 3	List of dialect words used in survey.	
p 4–10	Printed dialect word test – filled in by schoolchildren.	
p 11	Diagram of frequency of dialect words used in north of England.	
p 12	Letter from J. Dawson, headmaster of John Ruskin County Secondary School, Coniston, concerning dialect tests, and printed sheet of words.	
p 13	Completed dialect sheet.	
p 14–18	Written results of the 1965 dialect enquiry.	1965
p 19	'Survey of Dialect Words in Furness', *Evening Mail*, 2 January 1968.	1968
p 20	'Dialect Speech from Walney', *Evening Mail*, 25 January 1968.	1968
p 21	Letter from Mary Bond returning completed dialect quiz for the Burlington School, Kirkby-in-Furness 28 June 1968.	1968
p 22	Letters from W.B. Walls, headmaster of Ulverston Comprehensive School, 9 July and 10 October 1968 re dialect test.	1968
p 23	List of dialect words and answers.	
p 24	'Dialect Inquiry 2', by Ellen Fieldhouse, *Journal of the Dialect Society*, no 31 (December 1969) 7–12.	1969
p 25	Dialect article, *Guardian*, 23 December 1969. 'English dialect atlas planned', *Guardian*.	1969
p 26	Letters from Mrs. M.G. de Renzy-Martin, 27 January, 1 February, 8 February, 5 February 1970, 15 September, 4 November 1971.	1970– 1971
p 27	Letter from May and Joe Wills about *Journal of the Lakeland Dialect Society*, 31 March 1969.	1969
p 28	Letter from J.H.K. Losh, 11 February 1970 about dialect.	1970
p 29	Letter from Molly Richardson, 3 December, re dialect.	
p 30–31	Letters from Molly Richardson (2) re dialect.	1970
p 32	Postcard from Rev. J.A. Briggs, 5 January 1970.	1970
p 33	Letter from B. Wilkinson, 5 January 1970.	1970
p 34	Letter from J. Dawson, headmaster of John Ruskin School, Coniston, 15 June 1970.	1970
p 35–37	Lists of dialect words and phrases.	
p 38	Assessment of the schoolchildren's ability.	
p 39	Letter from D.A. Stanswood, head of English, Dowdales School, Dalton-in-Furness.	
p 40	Letter from J. Dawson of John Ruskin School, Coniston.	
p 41	List of dialect words – Upper Furness Usage.	
p 42	'Sheep Scoring Numerals' sheets, Yorkshire Dialect Society, 10 June 1967.	1967

p 43	'Mining Terms – Pit Ponies', article.	
p 44	Dialect sheet.	
p 45	'Domestic Servant, 50 years ago', by A. Cornthwaite, article.	
p 46	'Jubilate Deo', by J.C. Robinson, *Journal of the Lakeland Dialect Society*, no. 33 (1971) 25 (ph).	1971
p 47	'Oald Cumberland Customs' by John Sewell, *Journal of the Lakeland Dialect Society*, no. 33 (1971) 22.	1971
p 48	'Doomed Language', by J.D.U. Ward.	
p 49	Letter from J.C. Robinson, 31 July 1970.	1970
p 50–51	Letters (2) from W. Braithwaite, 11 and 20 August 1970.	1970
p 52–55	List of dialect words in *Journal of the Lakeland Dialect Society*.	
p 56–57	Letter from Stanley Ellis about student Mabel Round's M.A. Thesis on Furness.	
p 58–60	List and article about dialect phrases.	
p 61	Fieldhouse dialect tapes, newspaper article.	
p 62	Sheep counting, article.	
p 63	Sheep counting, article from *Country Life*, 22 July 1971.	1971
p 64	Article written by Joe Wills of Pennington, August 1971 about sheep counting.	1971
p 65	Letter from D.M. Richards to Joe Wills about sheep counting.	
p 66	Letter from Stanley [Raven], 10 November 1971.	1971
p 67	List of dialect words.	
p 68	'T' Joiners shop', by Harry Baines.	
p 69	'T' Ald Joiner's Shop', by Mrs. E.M. Lisseter, poem.	
p 70	'Lakeland Words' by Ellen Fieldhouse, *Journal of the Lakeland Dialect Society*, no. 33 (1971) (ph).	1971
p 71	'Lakeland Words' by B. Kirkby, (1898), *Journal of the Lakeland Dialect Society*, no. 33 (1971) 23–24.	1971
p 72–73	Experiment on dialect in schools, article.	
p 74	Diagram of distribution of dialect words in North of England.	
p 75	Birds copies from *Still the Real Lakeland* by A.M. Griffin (1970), article.	1970
p 76–77	Letter from Harry Griffin.	
p 78	'Were Tyan + Tyan ever Methera', by Michael Parkin, article.	
	'Folklore of grave digging', by Malcolm Stuart, article.	
p 79	Manx Language, article and letter, 5 June 1959.	
p 80	List of Hampshire dialect words.	
	Back cover : 'Is it nessy to make a donkey out of that lovely nirrup?', dialect article.	

6/16	*Scrapbook 16* Inside cover: 'Marsh Grange has links with history', *The News* (ph).	
p 1	'Departure of the Rev. G.W. Skyes from Rotherham for Kirkby in Furness', article. 'The Soldiers Prayer Book, Or A Pack of Cards spiritualised', article.	
p 2	'Kirkby twins' born 28 December 1919, newspaper photograph. Men at Burlington Slate Quarries, postcard. Notice for auction of property at Grizedale, by John Coward.	1919
p 3	Burlington School, article, 1966. Burlington School Prize Giving Day, typed notice. Presentation at Burlington School to headmaster leaving, article. Parish Magazine letter, October 1966. St. Cuthbert's Parish Calender, 1966–67.	1966 1966 1966– 1967
p 4	Funeral at St. Cuthbert's Church, Kirkby of Mr. John Fothergill Coward, *Barrow News*, 23 September 1966. Pastoral Letter from The Vicarage, Kirkby. Parish Boundary, Kirkby Ireleth – Broughton West, photograph.	1966
p 5	Pastoral Letter from the Vicarage, Kirkby Ireleth. 'Local Weather Sayings', poem. 'A Road across the Duddon Estuary', article.	
p 6	Lakeland Regional Young Farmers Club Rally, newspaper photograph. Pastoral Letter from the Vicarage, Kirkby, June 1967. Grizebeck Hill, newspaper letter. Grizedale bye-pass scheme, article. Church of Christ, Wall End, magazine photograph. Public Auctions at Kirkby by Alfred Coward, 16 June 1966, article.	 1967 1966
p 7	Kirkby newspaper cuttings 1966–1968 – Over 60's Club; Lent Suppers; Beckside Supper Club; Kirkby Ladies' Guild; Kirkby W.I.	1966– 1968
p 8	Kirkby Ireleth Literary Society 1967–1968 Syllabus. 'Grizebeck Sports hit by weather', article, June 1967. 'Wildfowlers rescued after three hours', article.	1967– 1968 1967

p 9	'More Entries for the Kirkby Show', *The News*, 23 August 1968.	1968
	Article on Grizebeck, *The News*, 8 December 1967.	1967
p 10–11	'Grizebeck Childrens Sports', 7 and 13 June 1968, newspaper photographs.	1968
p 12	'Annual Sports at Grizebeck', *Barrow News*, 7 June 1968.	1968
	'Grizebeck Annual Sports', *The News*, 13 June 1969.	1969
p 13	W.I. talk about Burlington Slate Quarries held at Beckside School, *The News*, 17 January 1969.	1969
	New Honorary Canons of Carlisle appointed, including Vicar of Kirkby, *Whitehaven News*, 17 April 1969.	1969
p 14	Duddon District Scots, article, with letter about Kirkby Scouts.	
	Church of Christ, Wall End, Kirkby-in-Furness, monthly newsletter, July 1969.	1969
p 15	'Furness Postal Delays', 27 June 1969.	1969
	Kirkby: Miss Legion competition, article.	
	Community Centre building plans, Parish Magazine.	
	School magazine article.	
p 16	Wildfowling on Woodland Fell at Birnie Tarn, *The News*, 8 August 1969.	1969
	Parish of St. Cuthbert, Kirkby Ireleth, Calendar 1969–70.	1969–1970
	Kirkby and District Floral and Horticultural Society Programme for the Annual Exhibition, 16 August 1969.	1969
p 17	Article: 'Row over Lakeland Shoots, bird lovers v wildfowlers' by Mary Stoker.	
	'Seeing the Countryside: Soutergate', by Ian Jones.	
	Funeral of Mrs. Agnes Coward of Kirkby Hall Farm, *The News*, 12 September 1969.	1969
p 19	'Seeing the Countryside: Kirkby-in-Furness', by Ian Jones, *The News*, 15 August 1969.	1969
p 20	Aerial photograph of Kirkby, *The News*, 5 September 1969.	1969
p 21	Kirkby W.I. talk on herbs, article.	
	Marriage of Miss June Ellershaw of Kirkby and Mr. George Waddington of Aldingham on 4 October, newspaper photograph.	
	Kirkby girl becomes Miss Legion at Grange, article.	
p 22	'Flower Arranger for 20 years: Mrs. Beatrice Murray of The Laurels, Kirkby-in-Furness', *The News*, 30 January 1970.	1970
p 23	Dialect, *Evening Mail* 31 December 1969.	1969
	Will of Mrs. Margaret Newton of Soutergate, Kirkby, article.	

	Dialect, *Guardian*, 22 December 1969.	1969
	Kirkby W.I.; Kirkby Mothers Union; Kirkby over 60's Club, articles.	
p 24	Pastoral Letter from the Vicarage, December 1969.	1969
	Advertisement for sale by A. Coward & Son, near Grizedale, *Barrow News*, 15 May 1970.	1970
	Kirkby W.I., *Barrow News*, 1 May 1970.	1970
	Letter from the Vicarage on New English Bible.	
p 25	The manorial court sitting of Victor Cavendish, Lord of the Manor of Kirkby, article.	
p 26	'Seeing the Countryside – Parish Church of St. Cuthbert, Kirkby', by W.G. McKelvey, *The News*, 3 April 1970, with accompanying letter.	1970
p 27	Quarrying Slate, *Guardian*, 14 May 1970.	1970
	Wedding of Miss M. Ellershaw of Low Hall Farm, Kirkby and Mr. Peter Quirk of Swarthmoor, 25 May 1970, newspaper photograph.	1970
p 28	Quiz on local names for the 4th Duddon Scout Group.	
p 29	Parish magazine June 1970. Kirkby Garden Party and Scouts, articles.	1970
	Kirkby Parish Council; Kirkby over 60's club; Kirkby Scout football team, articles.	
	Ship Inn, Kirkby, drawing, 29 May 1970.	
p 30	Kirkby-in-Furness, *The News*, 24 July 1970.	1970
p 31	Road between Ireleth and Kirkby, newspaper photograph.	
	Kirkby W.I.: Grizebeck sports day results; Film of Burlington Slate Quarries shown to Barrow Rotary Club, 13 November 1970, articles.	1970
	Notice from Burlington School activities for Autumn 1970.	1970
p 32	'Seashore gems from a Kirkby jewel factory', *The News*, 13 November 1970.	1970
	Kirkby poppy appeal, article.	
p 33	Kirkby W.I.; Kirkby over 60 club, articles.	
	Kirkby and District Floral and Horticultural Society, members ticket.	
	Programme for Kirkby and District Floral and Horticultural Society, 15 August 1970.	1970
	Calendar 1970–71 for St. Cuthbert's Church, Kirkby Ireleth.	1970–1971
p 34	Annette and Wade Kirby and John Robinson at Scar Bank, September 1969, photograph.	1969
	Kirkby Hall, July 1970, photograph.	1970
	Grizebeck Children's Christmas Treat Committee, article.	
	Greek lace-making in Furness, article.	

p 35	Kirkby Over 60 club; Kirkby Mothers Union; Kirkby W.I.; about Grizebeck Village Hall, articles.	
p 36	Reminiscences of Mrs. W., 84 years old, *The News*, 19 March 1971.	1971
	Complaint of Farmer at Duddon Bridge and Duddon Tidal Embankment Scheme, article.	
	Kirkby W.I., *The News*, 1971.	1971
	Village Hall's upkeep, 30 April 1971, article.	1971
p 37	Mole Catchers, *The News*, 2 April 1971.	1971
	Kirkby W.I., article and photograph.	
	Exhibition of work of Kirkby Adult Education Centre, newspaper photograph.	
p 38	Parish Magazine May 1971, extract.	1971
	Kirkby over 60s club; Kirkby Mother's Union, *The News*, 22 May 1971.	1971
	Kirkby Football Club, player of the year being awarded his prize, *Barrow News*, 28 May 1971.	1971
	Kirkby and Grizedale Old People's Welfare Committee, article.	
	Recipe winner from Kirkby, *Barrow News*, 23 July 1971.	1971
p 39	Children's Sports at Grizebeck, *Barrow News*, 18 June 1971.	1971
	Betsy Proctor, 18 months of Cross Beck Farm, Kirkby, photograph, *Barrow News*, 23 July 1971.	1971
	Death of Mrs. A. Muncaster, 101 years old, *The News*, 16 July 1971.	1971
p 40	Golden Wedding Anniversary of Mr. and Mrs. Edward Woodend, article and photograph.	
	Kirkby over 60s club, 2 April 1971.	1971
	Parish Magazine extract.	
p 41	Kirkby and District Floral and Horticultural Society's Annual Show, article.	1971
	Floral and Horticultural Society's Annual Show, 30 May 1971.	1971
	Programme for Kirkby and District Floral and Horticultural Society, 21 August 1971.	1971
p 42	Letter from Ellen Fieldhouse to Mr. S. Copple, bank manager, requesting information on bank's history (National Westminster), 28 July 1971.	1971
	Letter from S. Copple, 7 July 1971.	1971
	Notice to Kirkby residents of bank closure.	
p 43	Judith Illett of Avondale, Kirkby-in-Furness, teacher in Tunisia, *The News*, 27 August 1971.	1971
	Kirkby over 60s club.	

p 44	Clues for a quiz for the 4th Duddon Scout Group.	
p 45	The Church Book, *Parish Magazine*, November 1971.	1971
	Kirkby W.I.; Kirkby over 60s club, articles.	
	Kirkby in Furness W.I. quiz.	
p 46	Kirkby W.I., article.	
	Kirkby British Legion Children's party; Kirkby Royal British Legion children's party at Beckside Hall, *The News*, 17 December 1971, photographs.	
	Kirkby over 60s club, article.	
	Annual whist drive at Grizebeck, article.	
p 47	'Mother's Union', *The News*, 4 February 1972.	1972
	Mother's Union, Over 60s club, articles.	
	Church Magazine articles re theft of Church plate.	
	Mother's Union and Community Centre: February 1972.	1972
p 48	Old English Sheepdog wins at Crufts, owners from Kirkby (Mr. and Mrs. Jeffrey Chambers) *Vickers News*, March 1972.	1972 1972
	Kirkby W.I., article.	
	Back cover: Kirkby Mother's Union; Kirkby W.I.; Kirkby	
	Literary Society, articles.	
	Loose: Programme for Kirkby and District Horticultural Society Annual Exhibition on 19 August 1972.	1972

6/17	*Scrapbook 17*	
	Inside cover: 'History of Salthouse in Barrow', by J. Melville, *Evening Mail*, 16 February 1968.	1968
p 1	A Country Diary: Westmorland. *The Guardian*, 1 June 1968.	1968
	Stone inscribed with S.H. & Co., Park Mines, 1856, article, 12 April 1968.	1968
	Letter by Hazel Bayard about the fells where she lives.	
	Article on the country.	
p 2	'Ulverston – emporium of Furness, *Evening Mail*, 11 April 1968.	1968
p 3	'The Allithwaite Hermit: George Rhodes', 6 June 1968.	1968
	'Skidda', the hermit of Humphrey Head, newspaper photograph.	
p 4	'Princess Clementina': reputed daughter of Bonnie Prince Charlie (Newspaper correspondence).	
p 5	Furness Abbey painted in 1814 by Henry Edridge, article and photograph.	
	Roman sandals found during excavation at Hardknott, Cumberland, article.	

p 6   'Princess Clementina', letter in newspaper.
       History of Barrow – review of F. Barnes' work, article.
       Prehistoric trees at Blea Tarn, article.
p 7   Country Diary: Keswick, 'People and places in Lanca-
       shire', 'Brewing ale over 200 years', articles.
p 8   Barrow Town Hall *c.*1920, Early canon found at Walney
       before 1839, Piel Harbour as it was in 1832, newspaper
       photographs and print.
p 9   Old Inns – Black Dog near Dalton; King's Head of
       Broughton-in-Furness, drawings.
p 10   Furness Abbey Hotel, 22 December 1903; Furness Rail-
       way and Steamer Routes; Coaches descending Honister
       Pass, postcards.
p 11   'Holme Island's History', by W.E. Swale, article.
       The 'new bridge' in Barrow, newspaper photograph.
p 12   Discovery of a collar dated 1874 found in the parish
       church, Broughton, article.
       Pollen and its use in dating, article.
p 13   Broughton Fair, article.
       Morecambe Bay Hover Service, article.
p 14   Picking strawberries at Woodbine, Newton in 1917, *The*   1968
       News, 2 August 1968, photograph.
p 15   A Country Diary: The Lake District, article.
       'New contract for welding at Barrow Shipyard', *Guardian*   1968
       14 September 1968.
p 16   Pre-Conquest Abbey at Levens Hall, article.
p 17   Pre-Conquest Abbey at Levens Hall, article.
       Tidal bores from Arnside to Grange, *The Guardian*, 25   1968
       October 1968.
p 18   Vickers win contract for £10m. destroyer T42, 15 Novem-   1968
       ber 1968, article.
p 19   Excavation at old mote castle site at Aldingham, *The News*, 1968
       2 August 1968.
p 20   The Mote Castle at Aldingham, article.
p 21   Proposals for limiting traffic in the Lake District, article.
p 22   Winter in Furness, drawing, postcard and photograph.
p 23   Ramblers Association attempt to retain common land,
       article.
       'George Romney, Dalton's greatest son', article.
p 24   History of Grange local government, *The News*, 3 January   1969
       1969.
p 25   Houses in Grange by W.E. Swale, article.
p 26–27 'Churches and Schools at Grange', *The News*, 14 February   1969
       1969.

p 28	'When Grange water supply came from Wells and Springs', by W.E. Swales, *The News*, 24 January 1969.	1969
p 29	'Shrimp fishermen at Morecambe Bay', *The News*, 17 January 1969.	1969
p 30	Court Inquiry into Vickers strike, *The Guardian*, 12 February 1969.	1969
	Vickers Sports Club, *Vickers News*, 28 February 1969.	1969
p 31	Barrow Works Fire Brigade; Barrow Works Ambulance Corps annual dinner, article.	
	Retirement of Mr. R.W. Ward, manager of the Admiralty Department, article.	
p 32	Death of 'Freddie' Simpson, manager of Derby locomotive works, article.	
	North Lonsdale Society; Dalton-in-Furness Bone Club, articles.	
	Back cover: 'Docks, losing £2,000 a week – may close down', *The News*, 10 January 1969.	1969

6/18	*Scrapbook 18* Inside cover: 'John Ruskin' articles.	
p 1	John Ruskin, 29 March and 8 February 1969, articles.	1969
p 2	Exhibition at Hawkshead in the Old Courthouse, newspaper photographs.	
p 3	'Seeing the Countryside: Aldingham Hall' by Ian Jones.	
	Hoad Monument, Ulverston, 16 May 1969, article.	1969
p 4	5A girls at Victoria Girls School, Barrow in 1920, newspaper photograph.	1969
	'Stainton Quarry', drawing.	
	'Memories of Newton Mines', *The News*, 25 April 1969.	1969
p 5	Exhibition at the Coronation Hall, Ulverston, article.	
	'Seeing the Countryside: North Scale' by Ian Jones.	
p 6	Ulverston Hospital Parade group in 1928; Fourth King's Own Territorials; The Newby Bridge – Backbarrow by-pass; Last gas lamp in Dalton, 23 May 1969, old photographs.	1969
p 7	'Old Barrow' – Dalkeith Street, newspaper photographs.	
p 8	Dalton R.C. School (early 20th C); North Lonsdale Foxhounds Sponsored Walk, newspaper photographs.	
p 9	Lowick Show, *The News*, 28 March 1969, old photographs.	1969
p 10	Morecambe Bay Barrage Scheme, *The News*, 16 May 1969.	1969
p 11	The Spencer family of Poaka Beck, article.	
	Barrow Market, newspaper photograph.	

	'Dying Seabirds in North West', *The News*, 17 October 1969.	1969
	Vicar of Urswick with licence 1743, newspaper photograph.	
p 36	'Seeing the Countryside: Roosecote', by Ian Jones, *The News*, 24 October 1969.	1969
p 37	'New Factory Estate Plan for Barrow', article.	
	'William Fell's Journal: 1777', article.	
p 38	Dalton Green School, *The News*, 24 October 1969.	1969
p 39	George Fox Tercentenary and Ulverston, *The News*, 10 October 1969.	1969
p 40	'Seeing the Countryside: The Market Cross in Dalton' by Ian Jones, *The News*, 3 October 1969.	1969
	Back cover: 'Seeing the Countryside: Martin' by Ian Jones, *The News*.	n.d.

6/19	*Scrapbook 19*	
p 1	Furness Dialect.	
p 2	The dialect of High Furness	
	Letter to the Editor (1876) in dialect 'Polemics at Coniston!' (ph).	1876
p 3	Lakeland Dialect Society Service at Crosby Ravensworth Church, 9 June 1968.	1968
p 4	Furness dialect.	1954
p 5–7	Icelandic Place Names.	
p 8–9	'A Bit of Aw Maks' by Evelyn Metcalfe, *Lakeland Dialect Society Journal*, 42–44.	
p 9	Alexander Craig Gibson, 'A Champion of Cumbrian Dialect', Cumbria.	
p 10	'Amang T' Rownheeads', *North Lonsdale Magazine* (ph).	
p 11	'Farm Service', poem.	
	Norse Characteristics in Dialect.	
p 12	Song composed on the Whitehaven Town's Bill by Joe Hodgen in dialect (1859) (ph).	1859
p 13	'Lamplugh Jubilee Fox Hunt', by Joseph Hodgson, song in dialect, 1887 (ph).	1887
p 14–15	Bolton, John, 'The Ulverston Perpetual Tide Table' in dialect, *Lakeland Dialect Society Journal* (1950) pp 54–57.	1950
p 16–17	'Solomon's Song' (1869).	1869
p 18	'T' Invasion o' U'ston' from *Furness Past and Present* by Richardson (1880).	1880
p 19–21	'Cumberland and Westmorland – Weatherlore', poem by B. Kirkby (Kendal 1900).	1900

p 42	'Are You Gloppant?', 5 March 1956, article. List of dialect words.	1956
p 43	Letter, 15 March 1956, from C. Aspin, Hon. Secretary of Helmshore Local History Society enclosing the above sheet of dialect words.	1956
p 44	Lancashire and Yorkshire dialect, *Manchester Guardian* March 1956.	1956
p 45	Lakeland Dialect Society card for 1969. Tale about Harry Peel of Buttermere by John Peel, his grandson. Lakeland Dialect Society, article. Dialect words, extract from magazine.	1969
p 46–47	Northern Dialects, *The Guardian*, 22 April and 24 April 1970 (ph).	1970
p 48	Middle English Northern dialect, *The Guardian*, 5 May 1964 (ph).	1964
	Yorkshire Dialect Society, *The Guardian*, 21 May 1964 (ph).	1964
p 49	Dialect articles by Michael Parkin, *The Guardian*, 20 February, 18 August 1967, 9 January, 12 June 1968.	1967– 1968
p 50	'Vox Populi' – dialect article. Dialect, *The Guardian*, 27 December 1968 (ph).	1968
p 51	Yorkshire and Lancashire Dialect, *The Guardian*, 12 February 1968; 17 July 1969 (ph).	1968– 1969
p 52–57	Dialect stories: 'The Alert', 'The Income Tax Form', 'Billeting' (ph).	
p 58	Northern Dialect, *The Guardian*, February 1968. 'Word Mongering', *The Guardian*, 28 November 1970.	1968 1970
p 59	'Living Lancashire Phraseology', *The Times*, 14 October 1970.	1970
p 60	Advertisement in dialect from *Lancashire Annual* (1919) for Percival's Curiosity Shop, Elizabeth Street in Blackpool.	
p 61	'Queer Names of Turf Industry', article. Complementary card from *West Lancashire Evening Gazette*.	
p 62–67	Dialect words, *Blackpool Gazette and Herald*, 6 February– 24 April 1970.	1970
p 68	'The Haunted Windmill' by Teddy Ashton (in dialect).	
p 69	'Chaucer in the Yorkshire idiom', by Michael Parkin *The Guardian*. 'Old Yorkshire Expressions' by F.A. Carter, *Yorkshire Dialect Society*, 15.	
p 70	'Bite Bigger' – Yorkshire dialect poem.	
p 71	Diagrams of different word pronunciations in the North of England.	

List of West Riding words and expressions compiled by J. Varley Roberts in *Yorkshire Dialect Society Journal*.
'Chance Child', by Ian Dewhirst, poem.

p 72–73 Dialect article, 25 January 1970. *The Guardian.* 1970

Letter from Yorkshire Post Newspapers Ltd., 22 April 1969 enclosing photocopies of articles on dialect in the *Yorkshire Post*, 14 May 1969, and 24 December 1968. 1969

p 74 Letter from Ellen Fieldhouse to *Telegraph and Argus* 21 April 1970 concerning Buxom Betty dialect articles. 1970

'Awd Stowslay Toon' [mid 19th century North Riding Dialect], *Yorkshire Dialect Society Journal*, poem.

p 75 'T' Anniversary Dinner bi Buxom Betty', *Yorkshire Observer Budget*, 19 June 1953. 1953

'Yorkshire Sayin's' by W.R. Holloway (published 1913), *Yorkshire Dialect Society Journal*.

'More Half-Forgotten words' by H.W. Harwood, *Yorkshire Dialect Society Journal*.

p 76 'T' Higginbottams Whitsun Plans bi Buxom Betty', *Yorkshire Observer Budget*, 22 May 1953. 1953

'The Dialect of South Holderness' by Clare Ellin, *Yorkshire Dialect Society Journal*.

Short tale 'Roaked' by Pat Wilson, *Yorkshire Dialect Society Journal*.

p 77 'Yorkshire accent not for Americans', *The Guardian*, 1 May 1969. 1969

'Some almost forgotten words' by H.W. Harwood, *Yorkshire Dialect Society Journal*.

p 78 'Setterdy Neet – 60 years ago' by H.P. Brutton (1872–1947) from *Poetry from Sheffield 1750–1790*.

p 79 'From Owd Shevvild' from *Poetry from Sheffield 1750–1790*.

p 80 Stones 'Goodies' in N.E. Yorkshire Dialect in Walter F. Turner's book *Goodies and other Stories*.

Loose – *Some Words used in The Agrarian History of Cumberland* by R.S. Dilley, reprinted from the *Transactions of the Cumberland and Westmorland Antiquarian and Archaeological Society* (1970) NS LXX.

'Northumbrian speech' from *Northumbrian Heritage* by Nancy Ridley (London, 1969).

6/20 *Scrapbook 20*
Inside cover: 'Hilltop Diary', *Barrow News*, 25 April 1969. 1969
'Sketching with Stubbs' – bobbin mill at Woodside, near Waberthwaite.

	'Archaeology Talk: Newcastle in the Middle Ages'.	
p 1	'Portrait of the Duddon', article.	1969

Sketching with Stubbs, the former Vicarage at Ponsonby.
Holy Trinity Church, Millom; East Front, Millom Castle, postcards.

p 2   'Clash over a mock coffin protest' at Millom, 14 September   1968
1968.

Sketching with Stubbs, The Parish Church of St. Michael at Bootle.

p 3   Egremont Crab Fair and the Pulling Faces competition, article.

Sketching with Stubbs, Church of St. Michael, Workington.

p 4   The Place Names of Millom; Bishop to re-hallow Millom Church; articles.

p 5–6   The place names of Millom.

p 7   Millom Manorial Court Records, 2 parts.

Sketching with Stubbs, Church of St. Michael and all Angels at Isel, near Cockermouth.

p 8–9   'Millom Manorial Court Records', 3 parts.

p 10   'Sir Hugh Askew: The Gallant Wine Taster', *The News*, 29   1968
November 1968.

p 11–15   'The Violent Years', by Frank J. Carruthers, 5 parts.

p 17   Sketching with Stubbs at Mockerkin, 1 May 1969 and   1969
Eskdale.

Poet Norman Nicholson of Millom; article.

p 18   'Millom's new leather product should be bestseller', article.

Councillors look at new stamping machine at West Coast Tanneries, Haverigg, article.

p 19   Charity walk in West Cumbria for the Cystic Fibrosis Research Foundation Trust, article.

Hound Trail at Ben How, Whitehaven, newspaper photograph.

p 20   Exhibition of handicrafts held at the Rehabilitation Centre, Whitehaven.

Duke of Edinburgh Award Scheme exhibition in the   1969
Whitehaven Grammar and Overend Secondary Schools, *The Whitehaven News*, 15 May 1969.

p 21   Ellerside Secondary School Band, newspaper photograph.

Winner of the Music Festival at Whitehaven, newspaper photograph.

Women's Institutes, article.

p 22	'Frizington Hound Trials', *The Whitehaven News*, 15 May 1969.	1969
	Egremont Young Farmers' Club, newspaper photograph.	
p 23	Sketching with Stubbs at Silloth and the Croft, Kirksanton.	
p 24	'Oil Slick Operation on Cumberland Beaches', *The Whitehaven News*, 15 May 1969.	1969
p 25	Millom Pre-School Playgroup, *The Whitehaven News*, 22 May 1969.	1969
	Reunion of ex-Women's land army members at Gosforth, 22 May 1969, article.	1969
p 26	'Fun with Antiques at Gosforth'.	
	Photograph of Millom band, *c.* 1906, *The News*, 23 May 1969.	1969
	Cone commemorating the 50th Anniversary of the Forestry Commission near Whinlatter Pass, newspaper photograph, 29 May 1969.	1969
p 27	Sketching with Stubbs – Old Rectory at Gosforth.	
	Photograph of experts discussing cleaning Cumberland beaches of oil, *The Whitehaven News*, 29 May 1969.	1969
p 28	Sketching with Stubbs – Drigg Hall and Mirehouse by Bassenthwaite Lake.	
p 29	Aerial view of Bootle.	
p 30	Sketching with Stubbs, The Retreat, Whitehaven.	
	'Fight is on to save basket house from demolition', article.	
p 31	Charter granted to Ravenglass in 1209 by King John, *Evening Mail*, 5 July 1968.	1968
p 32	Patrick France in murder charge at Cleator Moor, near Whitehaven on 30 August 1884, article.	
	Back cover: Millom Ironworks taken over by Slough firm, *Whitehaven News*, 15 May 1969.	
	Sketching with Stubbs, St. Michael and All Angels at Torpenhow.	
	Plans for the Wordsworth Bi-Centenery.	
Addenda:		
a)	Ships of West Cumberland: 'Criffel' built at Maryport, 1891, article.	
b)	Aerial view of Haverigg.	
c)	Old beam engine in Whitehaven, article and photograph.	
d)	Sketching with Stubbs, Dawn in the Dale Bridge at Wasdale Head.	
e)	'The History of Hodbarrow Mines', *The News*, 28 February 1969.	1969
f)	Millom Ironworks closing, *Barrow News*, 16 August 1968.	1968

p 27	The new Michaelson Road High Level Bridge at Barrow. Vickers-Armstrongs staff excursion to Douglas, 7 July 1928, postcards.	1928
p 28	Lady of Mann, article and photograph. Lady Evelyn and Lady Moyra, Furness Railway Paddle Steamers, article and photograph.	
	Back cover: Maiden voyage of the Scythia, *The News*, 27 August 1921.	1921
	'Barrow from the Air – the Docks', *The News*, 27 August 1921.	1921

6/22	*Scrapbook 22* Inside cover: King Street, Ulverston, drawing. Tarn Hows, picture.	
p 1	Roanhead miners' gift of 1860, article.	
p 2	'The Manorial Court Records of Millom', articles.	
p 3	'Swans found covered in oil' in Cavendish Dock, Barrow, and 'House of Birds and Solitaire', article.	
p 4	Vickerstown and Vickers, newspaper photograph.	
p 5–6	'Seeing the Countryside', Leece Village and Hawcoat Village, by Ian Jones.	
	Robert Murray, T.U.C. Medical adviser comes to Barrow, *The Guardian*, 13 December 1969.	1969
p 7	'Bridge will be wider, safer', Friday 12 December. £245,000 grant for Barrow line, articles.	
p 8	Festive Tree at Dalton, Type 42 guided missile destroyer 'Sheffield' made at Barrow, 'He wants a "Save Barrow Society"', articles.	
p 9	Stainton Quarry, *The News*, Friday 16 January 1970.	1970
	'Farewell to a P. & O. Service', article.	
p 10	Nuclear submarine 'Churchill' docking at Barrow, *The Guardian*, 24 April 1970.	1970
	Dalton Day by Day, *The News*, 10 April 1970, photograph.	1970
	'Barrow's new road route', *The Guardian*, 4 February 1970.	1970
	'300 sign "save the Sun" petition'.	
p 11	'Need to improve the look of Furness villages, *The News*, 10 April 1970.	1970
	'Furness line not ruled out'.	
	'A Wintry March', 10 April 1970.	1970
	'North Lonsdale Society', article.	
	'Barrow to Fleetwood Ferry Soon', *The News*, 27 February 1970.	1970

p 12	The Abbots Room and Verandah of the Furness Abbey Hotel, and Dalton School Concert, newspaper photographs.	
p 13	'Traditional dance is revived'.	
	Children in Swarthmoor, taken July 1934, newspaper photograph.	1934
p 14	'Memory Corner': Rawlinson Street Boys' School, Barrow.	
	'Personality': Walter Shepherd.	
	'Grange attitude to link road'.	
p 15	Grand piano hoisted through fire escape doors of Countryside Theatre at Grizedale, newspaper photograph.	
	Dalton Book Club, article.	
	'Funeral Bill', victorian expenses; 'Barrow's Long Long link with subs'; 'Funeral biscuits', articles.	
p 16	'An Interesting but not unique old timetable'; 'A Friendly Railway', articles.	
p 17	'A Glimpse of History in Old Timetable', *The News*, 12 June	1970
	Old photograph of Dalton-in-Furness.	
p 18	Furness Drama Association playing 'Murder in the Cathedral', newspaper photograph.	
p 19	'Adventure base at Ulpha opened', *Barrow News*, 8 May 1970.	1970
	'Castle Armour', Dalton Castle, *Barrow News*, 8 and 22 May 1970.	1970
	Opening of Beckstones, a 16th C. farmstead in the Duddon Valley, *Barrow News*.	
p 20	'Barrow Shipbuilding Works', 1969.	1969
	A nuclear submarine at Barrow, 1969.	1969
	'Furness Farming 50 years ago', 8 May 1970.	1970
	'A New Lakeland Theatre'.	
p 21	Exhibition 70, held in Coronation Hall, Ulverston, 8 May 1970.	1970
	£150,000 improvements on the approach to the Barrow Works, 24 April 1970.	1970
	Memories of the Strand, 13 September 1970.	1970
p 22	'Baby Equipment for Cement Complex', *Vickers News*, 24 April 1970.	1970
p 23	'Iranian destroyer sails for contractors' Sea Trials', 24 July 1970.	1970
	Barrow-in-Furness ship docks, drawing.	
p 24	'The Strand, Barrow', article.	
	Travelling gantry crane, article and photograph.	1970

p 42	Furness Model Railway Club, article.	
	Threshing Machine, *The Westmorland Gazette*, 26 March 1971 photograph.	1971
p 43	Demolition of 'locomotive depot' at Foxfield station, *Evening Mail*, 12 February 1971.	1971
	Heraldic coats of arms and crests in Furness and Cartmel, article.	
p 44	'Barrow's team for "It's a Knock Out"', *The News*, 21 April 1971.	1971
	Dowdales Recorder Group, May 1971, newspaper photograph.	1971
p 46–48	Local Government Reform : Boundary changes, *The Guardian*, 17 February 1971.	1971
	Back cover: Ulverston Market Place, drawing.	
6/23	*Scrapbook 23*	
	Loose leaflets – *Vickers News*, 21 December 1973.	1973
p 1	'Mrs. Humphrey Ward's Furness Stories' by Norman Webster, *The News*, 4 September 1970.	1970
p 22	'Determination of Kirkby gardeners this Summer, 1972.	1972
p 3	'News Poetry Contest Prize Winners' by Irvine Hunt, *The News*, 18 August 1972.	1972
p 4	*Parish Magazine*, Kirkby Ireleth, August 1972.	1972
p 5	*Parish Magazine* Kirkby Ireleth, July 1972.	1972
	'Newby Bridge at the outflow of Windermere', *Cumbria* 1971.	1971
p 6	'Roanhead "The Thicket on the hill"' by James Melville, *The News*.	
p 7	'Morecambe Bay Barrage Schemes: Dual barrier favoured', *The Guardian*, 29 February 1972.	1972
p 8	'Constance Holme's Country', *The Field*, 24 August 1972.	1972
p 9	'Famous Barrow Shop, 60 years ago', by James Melville.	
p 10	'Market Street Dalton, 60 years ago', by James Melville, *The News*, 25 August 1972.	1972
p 11	'Lowick Show', *The News*, 8 September 1972.	1972
	'Press pulls visitors to Lakeland'.	
p 12	Abbot Hall Art Gallery, Progress report.	
p 13	Anthony Barker of Patterdale, Westmorland, *The Field*, 10 August 1972.	1972
	Cumberland and Westmorland Antiquarian and Archaeological Society, programme of events 1972.	1972
	'Barrage in Bay favoured', article.	
p 14	'Water, land and landscape' [Morecambe Bay].	

p 28   Advertisement for coffee and carols at the Church of Christ.

'Arnside Link Road Plan is Dropped', *The News*, 22 December 1972.   1972

Stonebreaker, J. Burns at work, article and photograph.   *c*.1898

Mr. and Mrs. James Sawrey from Springfield, Kirkby-in-Furness, on Golden Wedding anniversary.

p 29   Furness Track and Field Club, article.

The yachts on Walney Channel, *The News*, 26 January 1973.   1973

'Some railway memories' by W. Wood, *The News*, 5 January 1973.   1973

Letter from the vicar to the parishioners about a carol service.

p 30   'Over £5,000 for charities from Keswick Walk'.

'The Furness Packman'.

'Kirkby : Mother's Union'.

'Travelling packman or chapman'. articles.

p 31   'Lakeside line gets the green light'.

'Verdi's Requiem at Ulverston 'fantastic'.

'Country Diary, Keswick',

'Barrow housing plan seems to be getting off the ground', articles.

p 32   'Do you know this Furness Lane?' by James Melville, *The News*, 29 December 1972.   1972

Kirkby WI, 2 parts, 23 February 1973.   1973

'The doc and the locos', articles.

p 33   'Grant for Tytup Hall', *Evening News*, 25 April 1972.   1972

'Kirkby: Mothers Union; Poppy Appeal; Over 60s Club', articles.   1973

'Call to the North' talk at Kirkby.

Myles Newton, 85 years old, making swills, newspaper photograph.

Bob Heath's collection of Victorian prams, *Vickers News*, 23 March 1973.

p 34   'Leslie Sansom, tribute to a photographer', *Vickers News*, 20 December 1972.   1972

p 35   'Lakes Club Glider in Forced Landing', *The News*, 10 August 1973.   1973

Kirkby WI.

Vickers News, colour pullout of Vickers shipyards.

p 36   'New Inn, Biggar, closes this week 200 years of history,' *The News*, 20 April 1973.   1973

Kirkby, *The News*, 20 April 1973.   1973

Letter to the Editor answering 'Kirkby the scruffiest hamlet' letter.

	Kirkby WI.	
p 37	Kirkby Mother's Union; Kirkby Over 60s Club; Postcode for Barrow, articles.	
	Isle of Man as seen from Sandscale, Barrow.	
	Dowdales School Recorder Concert at the Morecambe Music Festival, newspaper photograph.	
p 38	The Royal Navy's 11th Nuclear Powered Fleet Submarine and photograph of the 'Sovereign', *Vickers News*.	
	Kirkby W.I.; Kirkby couple's 50 golden years; Derelict car near Kirkby, 8 June 1973.	1973
p 39	Millom Flower Show, *The News*, 21 September 1973.	1973
	New South Lakeland District, diagram.	
	Lakeland Dialect Society, article.	
	'Kirkby community centre gala day', *The News*, 15 June 1973.	1973
p 40	'MP favours Duddon mining', *The News*, 12 October 1973.	1973
	'A new probe for Duddon Iron Ore'.	
	'Mountain buses'.	
	'A centenary of launches slips by', *Vickers News*.	
p 41	'Weather hits entries at Kirkby Show', *The News*, 24 August 1973.	1973
	'Urswick puts clock back 400 years'; 'Coniston Quarry Plan'.	
p 42	Calendar for September, *Kirkby Parish Magazine*.	
	Records of baptism, confirmation, matrimony.	
	Log of camp at Silverdale by 4th Duddon Kirkby Cubs, 20–25 August 1973.	1973
	Printed letter from vicar at Penrith to people of Kirkby.	
p 43	Visit to a Chinese Exhibition in London.	
	Printed leaflet 'Kirkby in Furness: dates for your diary' 20 October – 17 November 1973.	1973
	'North Lonsdale Society'; 'Fire in Barrow', articles.	
	Kirkby over 60s Club', *The News*, 30 November 1973.	1973
p 44	Dalton Railway Station, article, and Robert Crookall, station master 1878–1922, and Miss Crookall, uniform staff, 1916, newspaper photograph.	
	'When Greenodd and Stainton had their own station-masters'.	
	'Furness Railway 1903–1910'.	
	Kirkby, lecture on Wedgewood China by Elsie Salmon.	
p 45	'Winter's Fury falls on Furness', *Evening Mail*, 29 November 1973.	1973
	Programme for Kirkby Ireleth literary society, 1973–1974.	1973–1974

p 57	'New Book on Lake Country Towns'.	1974
	Piel Island and Castle, articles, 21 and 28 June 1974.	1974
p 58	'Barrow Cornmill', article by James Melville, *The News*, 21 June 1974.	1974
	Kirkby Over 60's Club; Kirkby W.I.; Slate from Burlington Slate Quarries to be used for Arrad Foot By-pass.	
p 59	'How Michaelson Road, Barrow, got its name, by James Melville, *The News*, 7 June 1974.	1974
	Kirkby Parish Magazine.	
p 60	'Grizebeck Sports at Dove Ford', 14 June 1974.	1974
	Reminiscences of Mrs. Hannah Livesey 'collecting cockles on the shore'.	
p 61	Charity walk from Keswick to Barrow; Morecambe Bay Shrimp fishing; complaint over caravan parked at Duddon Bridge; Waste tips of Burlington Slate Ltd., Kirkby Ireleth.	
p 62	Mr. W. Burns of Barrow, article and photograph.	
	Engineering Works receives the Order of St. John.	
	John Wannell, manager of catering services at Vickers House.	
	Vickers wins contract for explosive cutting of holes in the BP.	1974
	Forties Oil Pipeline, *Vickers News*, 28 June 1974.	
p 63	'Making Besoms or Birch Brooms in Furness' by James Melville, *The News*, 14 June 1974.	1974
p 64	Decline of Morecambe Bay Fisheries.	
	'Low Timber Cart at Bank End at entrance to Duddon Valley' by James Melville, *The News*, 8 March 1974.	1974
p 65	Duke of Edinburgh Award Scheme, *Vickers News*, June 1974.	1974
p 66	'Kirkby Sports', 5 July 1974.	1974
	Walk to Hard Knott Fort.	
	Robert Southey, bicentenary, in Keswick.	
p 67	Golden Wedding for childhood friends, *Barrow News*, 9 September 1974.	1974
	Woodburn's corn mill at Ulverston, Cumbria, 16 August 1974.	1974
	Port Haverigg development scheme, newspaper photograph.	1974
p 68	Hartley's Brewery at Ulverston, by Martin Lawson.	
	'Woodburn corn mill may be a museum'.	
p 69	Exhibition of family papers at Holker Hall.	
	Irvine Hunt, poet, signing autographs at Hawkshead.	

	Councillors looking at Glannoventa – Roman boat house at Ravenglass.	
	Ulverston dairy report.	
	No grant for transferring Barrow Docks to Vickers, article.	
p 70	Broughton children at proclamation ceremony, *Barrow News*, 9 September 1974.	1974
	Hound trails in Furness, 23 September 1974.	
p 71	Article on Mrs. May Stevenson and her paintings of Furness, *The News*, 2 August 1974.	1974
	Ulverston dairy report, *The News*, 26 July 1974.	1974
	Welding Engineering, 26 August 1974.	1974
	Death of Richard Pickering, *Parish Magazine*.	
p 72	North Lonsdale Society article, 23 August 1974.	1974
	Duddon from Kirkby Fell, poem, 30 August 1974.	1974
	Kirkby W.I.	
	Air survey of Solway Firth, 30 August 1974.	1974
	Life of Master Mariner and Pilot Guy Charnley, 23 August 1974.	1974
p 73	'Grange Promenade followed Railway', by James Melville, *The News*, 30 August 1974.	1974
p 74	'Kirkby Flower Show, *Barrow News*, 23 September 1974.	1974
	Children at Barrow Arts Centre, 23 September 1974.	1974
p 75	Lord Richard Cecil, article, 2 August 1974.	1974
	'Life on the Railway over 50 years ago', by W.H. Lindsay, 30 August 1974.	1974
p 76	'Ulverston Old Mill project', 23 August 1974.	1974
	Back cover: 'Dalton children produce own paper', *The News*, 23 August 1974.	1974
	Loose: Early days of the Furness Railway.	
6/24	*Scrapbook 24* Inside cover: Article 'Steamers in the Bay' by Frank Walmsley.	
	Steamers, postcard.	
	Barrow ships, article.	
p 1	H.M.S. Cumberland; P. & O. R.M.S. Strathedes; P. & O. S.N. Co Liner 'Strathaird', articles.	
p 2–31	Series of 'Barrow Ships' articles: Nos 1–13, 24, 26–29, 31, for the ships City of Rome, The Orizaba, Nordenfelt, The Monarch, The Hainaut, Empress of Japan, H.M.S. Powerful, H.M.S. Niobe, The Mikasa, Manxman, H.M.S. Vengeance, H.M.S. Vanguard, H.M.S. Revenge, Jervis Bay, The Rurik, Scottish Mine, H.M.S. Cumberland, Orient Liner Orama, Scythia,	

Lady of Mann, Kedah, The Sao Paulo, Ben-my-Chree, Strathnaver, Rangatire, Queen of Bermuda, H.M.S. Ajax, Almirante.

p 30   'More about The Kedah, the ship with a glamorous battle history'.

'When Strathaird was a trooper'.

'Last days of Barrow-built liner Queen of Bermuda.'

Back cover: Barrow Ships series no. 45, Methane Princess.

Loose: 'Royal visit to Barrow' (Princess Margaret), *Vickers News*, July 1967.   1967

Barrow Centenary – double page pull out.

H.M.S. 'Resolution', 2 October 1967, article.   1967

6/25   *Scrapbook 25*

p 1–28   Series of articles 'Ships of West Cumberland': Nos. 1–29 for the towns and companies: Whitehaven, Harrington, Maryport, Workington, Lancaster, Brocklebank Cunard Ltd., Cape Horners Vessels, The Lowca, The Mallgate, The Harrington, John Peal, Ritsons Yards at Maryport, The Peter Iredale Ship, The Criffel sailing barque, the Moresby, the Alice A. Leigh ship, the Wray Castle, J. Fell of the Harrington and Workington Shipbuilding and Ropemaking Company, R. Williamson and Co., Boarding House Masters and crimps, The brig Congress.

BD/F 7

Newspaper Cuttings

This section was originally loose newscuttings. But the items have now been re-organised into four additional scrapbooks, plus a folder containing six larger items. In the case of the scrapbooks, or newspaper cutting books, the subjects of the various cuttings are shown here against the page numbers.

1   Copy of *The Barrow Guardian* (complete newspaper) 29 November 1913.   1913

2   *Newspaper Cutting Book 7/2*   1939–1973

p 1   'Air Minister's plan forced down of fell: Sir Kingsley Wood shaken and Air Marshall injured'. *The Guardian*, 29 July 1939 (ph).   1939

p 2	Train crash at Kirkby-in-Furness, *Daily Express* (ph).	1939
p 3–4	School bus accident at Broughton-in-Furness, *c.* February 1962; 12 cuttings.	1962
p 4	'Mummers find locked doors'. *The Guardian*, 1 January 1963.	1963
p 5	'Pace-egging in the Grand Tradition', *The Guardian*, 13 April 1963.	1963
p 5	Children rolling Easter 'pace eggs', *The Guardian*, 31 March 1964 (ph).	1964
p 6	'When Mumming was all the Rage at Whitehaven,' *Evening Mail*, 14 December 1965.	1965
p 7	'Pace-egging play', *Evening Mail*, 1 April 1966.	1966
p 7	Flooding in West Cumberland and the Furness area, *The Times*, 28 February 1967.	1967
p 8	'Seeing the Countryside' by Ian Jones, No. 1, Pennington Church 1969, *The Barrow News*.	1969
p 9	'Seeing the Countryside' by Ian Jones, No. 14, Rampside, *The News*, 8 August 1969.	1969
p 10	'Seeing the Countryside' by Ian Jones, Newton-in-Furness. *The News*, 10 October 1969.	1969
p 11–16	'Furness surnames and their stories, origins, trades and travels': a series of articles by Dr. J.D. Marshall, *Barrow News*, 27 February–20 March 1970.	1970
p 17	'Boney's Wars brought riches to Furness Farm': further article by Dr. J.D. Marshall, *Barrow News*, c. March 1970.	1970
p 18	'I search in vain for a Hawkshead Wigg', by Brenda Colton, *The News*, 5 February 1971.	1971
p 19	'Making Fig Sue and Salmon Scouse', by Brenda Colton, *The News*, 14 May 1971.	1971
p 20	Letter to *The News* on the subject of Hawkshead Wiggs by V.J.H. Coward, and reply with short article by Mrs. Eileen Jay; February 1971.	1971
p 21	Local dishes recalled by an Ulverston widow; newspaper article.	1971
p 22	Rampside Station; article by J. Melville, *Barrow News*, 8 January 1971.	1971
p 22	Letter to *The News*: 'More memories of Rampside Station' by Harry Pittaway.	1971
p 22	Letter to *The News*, 'When trains ran to Rampside'.	1971
p 23	'The Oversands Refuge and its Folly': article about Chapel Island by J. Melville, *Evening Mail*, 2 April 1971.	1971
p 24	'Wells of Romance and Legend', by J. Melville, *Evening Mail*, 23 April 1971.	1971

p 25	'Bidding mourners to a Funeral', by J. Melville, *Evening Mail*, 10 March 1972.	1972
p 26	'Guide across the Sands to Chapel Island', by Brenda Colton, *The News*, 17 November 1972.	1972
p 27	'B.B.C. goin' to Isle O'Dogs'; article about the changing language in Britain, *The Guardian*, 21 September 1972.	1972
p 27	'Future of Piel Castle', *The News*, 23 July 1971.	1971
p 27–28	'The Ghosts of Piel Island', *The News*, 21 December 1973.	1973
p 29–34	Rescue of the Pisces II, belonging to Vickers Oceanics, September 1973 (9 cuttings).	1973
p 33–34	'Sheep counting in Cumbria'; 4 letters to *The Guardian*, September 1973.	1973
3	Copy of *The Barrow News* special strike edition, 26 July 1959.	1959
4	Album of cuttings relating to the 'Vinland Expedition' of the 'Griffin,' sponsored by *The Guardian* newspaper, with other items concerning Viking expeditions to North America, 1966.	1966
5	'Barrow's Centenary 1867–1967': special supplement issued by *North Western Evening Mail*, 1967.	1967
6	'Barrow Centenary Album 1967': supplement issued by *Barrow News & Mail Ltd.*, September 1968.	1968
7	'Barrow's New Market': *News* Series Trade Supplement, 9 July 1971.	1971
8	Envelope containing incomplete series of newspaper articles on Barrow built ships, Nos. 31, 32, 34–34, 39–44, 46, 47, which relate to the ships President Peron; Oriana; 'Tale of the Tankers'; Resolution; Himylaya; Dreadnought; Accra; Seraph; Strathmore; Carl Schmedeman; 'The Empire Ships'; Teal; Hinemoa; Illustrious; 'South American survey'. Published in *Barrow News*, June–October 1969.	1969
9	*Newspaper Cutting Book 7/9*	
p 1	'All the World wants Kirkby Slate'; *The News*, 13 August 1971.	1971
p 2	'Furness Farmer looks back on the "Dirty Thirties"',	1971

	memoirs of a former farmer at Conishead Priory, now living in Canada, *The News*, 26 November 1971.	
p 3–4	Article on 'Cumbria's West Coast'; *The Guardian*, c.1974.	1974
p 5	'Morris Men provide a touch of tradition', *The News*, 4 April 1975.	1975
p 6	'Train drivers reading while driving the train'; pieces from *Barrow News*, 12 September 1975.	1975
p 6	'Train drivers reading when driving the train'; from *The Guardian*, 6 September 1975.	1975
p 6	'Prospect of fight over Duddon'; 4 April 1975.	1975
p 7	An early photograph of Broughton; *The News*, 28 March 1975.	1975
p 8–15	Series of 10 extracts from the diaries of John B. Moore of Hallthwaites, 1882; published in *The News*, 12 September–14 November 1975.	1975
p 16	'The Mary Goldsworthy', by Trevor Morgan; *Barrow News*, 25 June 1976.	1976
p 17	'Barrow Station as it looked about 1914'; by J. Melville.	n.d.
p 17	'Pace Egg according to Midgley', by Michael Parkin.	n.d.
p 18–34	Weekly newspaper column 'Embracing Arms and the origin of Surnames' by Bill Nunney, covering the surnames Abel, Abbot, Acton, Andrews, Ashley, Austin, Atwood, Barker, Bridges, Carpenter, Chapman, Drake, Ellis, Everett, Fletcher, Green, Inglis, King, Lambert, Marshal, Mason, Matthews, Moore, Morton, Norris, Palmer, Osborne, Pollard, Russell, Salter, Taylor, Watson, Williams, Wilson.	n.d.

10	*Newspaper Cutting Book 7/10*	n.d. c.1960's–70's
p 1	'The Romany Language', by Peter Rogers.	
p 2–3	'School life in Victorian Days', by Kathleen Stevenson.	
p 4	'Sketching with Stubbs at Lamplugh'	
p 4	'Travel from Roa Island station'; letter by T. West.	n.d.
p 5	'Kirkby Literary Society: Kirkby Night', short article.	
p 5	Cuttings (3) about Common rights in Kirkby Ireleth.	
p 6	Cutting showing Dalton Church in Victorian times, before rebuilding.	
p 7	Article: 'Morris men tour Furness with Play'.	
p 8	Cutting with photograph of Furness Morris Men playing in Market Square, Ulverston.	
p 9	Old Rampside Station and Piel (Roa Island) Station; newspaper photographs.	

(BD/F 7)

p 10   'The January Blizzard'; piece from *Barrow News*, n.d.
p 11–16   'Park your Car and Take A Walk': articles (6) by 'Furness
           Rambler' covering Grizebeck; Oxen Park; Abbot's
           Reading; Broughton Beck; Beacon Tarn; Windmill
           Hill.

BD/F 8

8/1–48 Printed matrial (mainly 19th Century)

This is an assortment of printed booklets collected by Mrs. Fieldhouse, together
with some cuttings which she had inserted into card covers. The section forms a
single bundle.

8/1–48   *Printed material*: (mainly 19th century)

1   *The Shepherd's Guide or a Delineation of the Wool and Ear*   c.1820
           Marks of the Different Stocks of Sheep (Penrith c.1820).

2   *Lamplugh Club*, by a Looker On (Whitehaven, 1856)   1856
           intended to assist in preserving a faithful record of the
           dialect of the neighbourhood of Whitehaven.

3   *The Wild Dog of Ennerdale*, (Whitehaven, 1864).   1864

4   Joe His-sel, *Joe and the Geologist, and T' Reats On't*   1867
           (Carlisle, 1867) new edition.

5   *T' Invasion o' U'ston: A Sketch in the Furness Dialect*   1867
           (Carlisle, 1867).

6   *T' Lebby Beck Dobby: A Sketch in the Furness Dialect*   1867
           (Carlisle, 1867).

7   *T'Siege o' Brou'ton: A Sketch in the Furness Dialect* (Car-   1867
           lisle, 1867) by a native.

8   Willcox and Gibbs Sewing Machine Co. advertisement   1870
           (1870).

9   Robinson, William of Head Cragg, Kirkby Ireleth, *Poems*   1871
           and Hymns (Ulverston, 1871).

10   *Cassell's Popular Educator*, new issue, October 1876 –   1876–
           March 1877, parts 1–6.   1877

11   *Book of Words*: to be sung by the Leeds Harmonic Union at   1878
           the Entertainments given by His Grace the Duke of
           Devonshire to the parishioners of Kirkby Ireleth on the
           occasion of the Public Opening of the Burlington
           Schools, 24–26 April 1878 (Skipton, 1878).

12   *Cassell's Family Magazine*, March 1878, advertisements for   1878
           Camomile Pills, Pears' Shaving Soap and Dr. Rooke's
           Medicines.

13	Hartley, John, *The Original Illuminated Almanack* (London, 1878).	1878
14	Carter's Seeds advertisements (1880).	1880
15	*Cassell's Family Magazine* advertisements. January 1880.	1880
16	*Cassells' Family Magazine* (1880) Article entitled 'Modern Dress Reformers' and 'What to Wear: Chit Chat on Dress' by our Paris correspondent.	1880
17	Wilson, Sir Charles, W., ed., *Picturesque Palestine*: [New Illustrated Work on the Holy Land] (London 1880) [advertisement].	1880
18	Collingwood, W.G., 'Ulpha Old Hall', *Transactions of the Cumberland and Westmorland Antiquarian and Archaeological Society*, (1881) V, 315.	1881
19	Cash's Embroidery Frilling advertisements – woven initials and names, collars, cuffs and fronts, etc.	1881
20	Lees, Rev. Thomas, 'Cresset Stone at Furness Abbey: A Correction', *Transactions of the Cumberland and Westmorland Antiquarian and Archaeological Society* (1882, VI, 310–11	1882
21	The Quiver Advertising Sheet (1881).	1882
22	Fell, John, 'The Guides over the Kent and Levens Sands, Morecambe Bay', *Transactions of the Cumberland and Westmorland Antiquarian and Archaeological Society* (1883) VII 1–26.	1883
23	*Neddy's Courtship an' Neddy's Rival*, by a Lancashire Lad (London, 1883).	1883
24	Rigge, Henry Fletcher, 'Notes from Cartmel Church', *Transactions of the Cumberland and Westmorland Antiquarian and Archaeological Society*, (1883), VII, 103–08.	1883
25–27	*Great Northern Railway: Tourist Arrangements from London* (1885).	1885
	London and North Western Railway Programme of Tourist Tickets (1885).	1885
	Midland Railway Programme of Tourist Arrangements 1 June 1885).	1885
28	Ellwood, Rev. T., 'Notes upon some of the older Word Forms to be found in comparing the language of Lakeland with the language of Iceland,' *Transactions of the Cumberland and Westmorland Antiquarian and Archaeological Society*, (1887) IX, 383–92.	1887
29	Ferguson, Chancellor, 'Cockfighting', *Transactions of the Cumberland and Westmorland Antiquarian and Archaeological Society*, part 2, (1888) IX, 366–82.	1888
30	Cowper, H.S., 'Law Ting at Fell Foot, Little Langdale,	1889

Westmorland', *Transactions of the Cumberland and Westmorland Antiquarian and* Archaeological Society (1889), II, 1–6.

31   Hartshorne, Albert, 'Notes on the Postlethwayts of   1889
Millom, with reference to an early Initialled Spoon of that family', *Transactions of the Cumberland and Westmorland Antiquarian and Archaeological Society*, OS, (1889) X, 44–52.

32–33   Ellwood, Rev. T., 'The Reeans of High Furness', vol 2,   1890
Transactions of the Cumberland and Westmorland Antiquarian and Archaeological Society, (1890) II, 368–98.

Fell, John, 'Some illustrations of Home Life in Lonsdale   1890
North of the Sands, in the 17th and 18th centuries', *Transactions of the Cumberland and Westmorland Antiquarian and Archaeological Society* (1890), II, 368–98.

34   Calverley, Rev. W.S., 'Pre-Norman Cross-Shaft at   1893
Heversham', *Transactions of the Cumberland and Westmorland Antiquarian and Archaeological Society*, (1893) XII, 118–24.

35   Cowper, H.S., 'Gleaston Castle', *Transactions of the Cumberland and Westmorland Antiquarian and Archaeological Society* O.S. (1893) XIII, 37–51 (extract).   1893

36   Collingwood, W.G., 'Manuscript [17th century] Epistles   1895
of Early Friends', *Transactions of the Cumberland and Westmorland Antiquarian and Archaeological Society*, (1895) XIII, 155–59.

37   Cowper, H.S., 'Sites of Local Beacons: Cumberland and   1895
Westmorland: Lancashire North of the Sands', *Transactions of the Cumberland and Westmorland Antiquarian and Archaeological Society* (1895) XIV 139–44.

38   Cowper, H.S., and the President, 'Sites of Local Beacons: 1896
Cumberland and Westmorland and Lancashire North of the Sands', *Transactions of the Cumberland and Westmorland Antiquarian and Archaeological Society* (1896), XIV, 139–43.

39   Cowper, H.S., 'A relic of Pennington Old Church',   1898
Transactions of the Cumberland and Westmorland Antiquarian and Archaeological Society, (1898), XV, 312–14.

40   Ellwood, Rev. T., 'The Mountain Sheep: their origin and   1898
marking', *Transactions of the Cumberland and Westmorland Antiquarian and Archaeological Society*, (1898) XV, 1–8.

41   Brierley, Ben (Ab-o'th'-yate) *Heaw to do beaut coal* (Oldham).

42	Edmondson, T., ('Tot Spot'), *Comic Poems and Recitations* (Dalton-in-Furness.)
43	Feldman's *Easiest Book of Kiddie's Carols* (London).
44	*Olga's Valentine* by the author of *The Diary of a Plain Girl*, 152–56.
45	Feldman's *Album of Kiddie's Nursery Rhymes* (London).
46	*Philips' Series of large Sixpenny Maps* (London) [advertisement].
47	*The Leisure Hour Advertisement Sheet*, with Provident Life Office, Clerical Medical and General Life Assurance Society, The Clergy Mutual Assurance Society.
48	*Tommy-the-Bobbin-Carrier's 'Chep Trip to th' Sawt Wayter'* by John Almond. n.d.

BD/F 9

9/1–68 Printed material: 20th century.

This is more recent material than the previous section, and items vary in scale from leaflets to complete books. They form three bundles of smaller items, together with two final larger items.

9/1–68	*Printed material*: 20th century	
1	Woodhouse, John, and Briggs, Henry, *A Short History of the Kirkby- in-Furness Equitable Industrial Co-operative Society Ltd. 1861–1911* (Manchester, 1912).	1912
2	Leaflet describing St. Cuthbert's Church, Kirkby Ireleth, by the Vicar, June 1922.	1922
3	Anon., *Lad's Love: A Drama of Westmorland Village Life in Four Acts* (Grasmere, 1925).	1925
4	*Vickers Limited Marine Engine Draughtsmen's 28th Annual Dinner* held in The Victoria Park Hotel, Barrow-in-Furness, 17 December 1927.	1926
5	Voller, K.A., ed., *Practical Processes for Garment Making and Simple Upholstery*, third edition, revised (Gloucester, 1927).	1927
6	Bennett, Rodney, *Let's Do a Play* (London, 1933).	1933
7	Wilder, Thornton, *The Happy Journey* (London, 1934).	1934
8	Programme for the 'Halle Concerts Society Pilgrim Trust Concert', 18 August 1940.	1940
9	Pamphlet:, *The Church of Saint Mary and Dalton Tower* by L.D. (1944) [2 copies].	1944

10	*The Church of Saint Michael and the Holy Angels, Penn-ington* by L.D. (1944).	1944
11	*The Church of Saint Mary, Parish Church of Ulverston* by L.D. (1944).	1944
12	*The Church of Saint Mary and Saint Michael, Urswick* by L.D. (1944).	1944
13	*The Church of St. Cuthbert, Aldingham*; clip with leaflets (3 editions) and printed sketch.	1928; 1944; n.d.
14	Programmes for concerts: North Lonsdale Combined Choirs (14 April 1945); North Lonsdale Combined Choirs (19 April 1947): Kirkby Choral Group Concert (10 April 1947); North Lonsdale Combined Choirs (17 April 1948); Ulverston Choral Society (11 May 1951).	1945–51
15	Garton, S.J., *Furness Abbey* (London, 1950).	1950
16	Barnes, F., *Barrow and District: An Illustrated History* (Barrow-in-Furness, 1951).	1951
17	Melville, J., and Hobbs, J.L., *Early Railway History in Furness* (Kendal, 1951) reprinted from the *Transactions of the Cumberland and Westmorland Antiquarian and Archaeological Society*, XIII (1894).	1951
18	Cowx, J., ed., *The Kendal Cookery Book* (Kendal, 1951).	1951
19	Programme for the Institution and Induction of Rev. John Ronald Norman to the Rectory of Greystoke, 15 October 1955.	1955
20	Programme and Order of Service for the *Diocese of Carlisle Pilgrimmage to the Shrine of Saint Cuthbert and the Tomb of the Venerable Bede*, 25 May 1957.	1957
21	Programme for *A Cycle of Mystery Plays*, adapted by Rev. W.A. Batty and Rev. O.G. Vigeon (7–12 July, 1958).	1958
22	Hobbs, J.L., *The Journal of John Wilson Soulby of Ramp-side Academy* (Kendal, 1960) reprinted from the *Trans-actions of the Cumberland and Westmorland Antiquarian and Archaeological Society*, New Series, LX.	1960
23	*The Raven* (Downside School Magazine) 1960: obituary to former pupil Dr. R.A. Parsons 1885–1960.	1960
24	Notices (3) of the funerals of the late Henry MacPhail, John Alanach and John Ross of Grantown-on-Spey, Morayshire, 21 February and 10 March 1962.	1962
25	Anon., *Burlington Blue-Grey Slate* (London) reprinted from *The Quarry Managers' Journal*, November 1964.	1964
26	Dickinson, J.C., *Furness Abbey, Lancashire* (London, 1966).	1966

27	Dickinson, R.F., *The Friendly Society of the Inhabitants of the Parish of Lamplugh and its Neighbourhood* (Kendal, 1966) reprinted from the *Transactions of the Cumberland and Westmorland Antiquarian and Archaeological Society*, New Series, LXVI.	1966
28	Pamphlet, *Common Land and Town and Village Greens* (Swinton, 1966).	1966
29	Pamphlet, *Vinland Adventure* (Guardian, 1966).	1966
30	Pamphlet, *The Death Warrant of King Charles I*, Historic Parliamentary Documents Reproduction, no. 7 (HMSO 1966).	1966
31	Gascoigne, Margaret, *Discovering English Customs and Traditions* (Tring, Hertfordshire, 1969).	1969
32	Booklet, *Vickers Centenary: 1867–1967*.	1967
33	Magazine, *H.M.S. Resolution: Ballistic Nuclear Submarine* (1967).	1967
34	*V.S.G. Link*, no. 6, 1969 (winter).	1969
35	*Vickers News*, 26 June 1970.	1970
36	*V.S.G. Link*, no. 7, 1970 (spring).	1970
37	*Vickers News* (4) 22 January – 25 June 1971.	1971
38	*Voyage to Mayaluum* (New York, 1972), with accompanying letter from J.L. Kirby to Ellen Fieldhouse, 15 January 1973.	1972
39	*Vickers News*, 28 September 1973.	1973
40	M.T.S. Argonaut, cruising yacht, pamphlet.	1973
41	Kirkby and District Floral and Horticultural Society Annual Exhibition programme, 17 August 1974.	1974
42	*Vickers News* (2), 28 February and 27 March 1975.	1975
43	The Patent Office, *A Century of Trade Marks* (London, 1976).	1976
44	Advertisement for above book, with letter enclosed, 23 January 1976 from the Patent Office.	1976
45	*The Trade Marks Journal*, vol. 101 (5 May 1976).	1976
46	*The Trade Marks Journal : Centenary Souvenir 1876–1976*: List of applications for the registration of trade marks under the Trade Marks Registration Act 1875.	1976
47	Mitchell, W.R., *Across Morecambe Bay: by the Oversands Route* (Clapham, 1973).	1973
48	*Vickers News*, 29 April 1977.	1977
49	*V.S.G. Link*, May 1977.	1977
50	Anon., *Address of the Reformers of Fawdon to their Brothers the Pitmen, Keelmen, and other Labourers on the Tyne and Wear* (Newcastle Upon Tyne, 1819).	1819

51	Anon., *Molly Migg's Trip to the Seaside: the Adventures and Misadventures of a Country Lass*, 4th edition (London).	n.d.
52	Beckside School Committee : Notice of a sale of furniture and household goods, 27 November.	n.d.
53	Cumberland and Westmorland Antiquarian and Archaeological Society: News letter and list of regional specialists, November 1968.	1968
54	Douglas Bolton, G., magazine article on Cumberland from '*The Counties of Britain*' series.	n.d.
55	Dyson, Ben., and Ellis, Stanley, *Yorkshire Pudding Olmenack: A Mixture of Early Yorkshire Almanacs* (Ilkley, Yorkshire).	n.d.
56	Fieldhouse, Ellen, *The Parish Church of Saint Cuthbert, Kirkby Ireleth* – illustrated guide (3 copies).	n.d.
57	Morris, J.P., *A Handy Guide to the Ruins of Furness Abbey* (Ulverston)., early 20th cent.	n.d.
58	Observer Supplement, '*The Triumph of the British*', 12 parts.	n.d.
59	Observer Supplement, '*The Making of the British*', 10 parts.	n.d.
60	Radford, P.J., *Old Maps*.	n.d.
61	Stables, Matthew, *Kirkby Ireleth: Musings* (Millom).	n.d.
62	*The Virginian*, vol 1, no. 1., Spring 1970.	1970
63	*Attack on Inflation: A Policy for Survival* (HMSO), pamphlet.	c.1976
64	Advertisement for William Hutchinson's *The History of the County of Cumberland* with introduction by C. Roy Huddleston.	1974
65	Mappa Mundi in Hereford Cathedral, pamphlet, ? July 1961.	?1961
66	*Yorkshire Dales National Park: Mines*, pamphlet.	n.d.
67	Folder with incomplete series of Kirkby Ireleth parish magazines and newsletters, 1900–1951.	1900–1951
68	*Heraldry of the Kirkby and Kirby families:* bound monograph by J.L. Kirby, commenced 1964; revised and completed 1973–74.	1964–1974

BD/F 10

10/1–14 Photographs.

The views in this section are mainly of local interest. There are varying sizes, enclosed in one large envelope.

1	Aircraft crash on Kirkby Moors in which the Air Minister, Sir Kingsley Wood, was travelling, 28 July 1939. Small photograph and negative, enclosed with accompanying letter dated 25 November 1958 from the Librarian of the *Manchester Guardian*.	1939
2	Train crash at Kirkby-in-Furness station (3 views) 25 August 1939, damaged locomotive, general view and some of the wreckage.	1939
3	Sir Joshua Kirkby and wife, painting by Thomas Gainsborough, mid 18th Century. Reproduction posted 14 February 1969. [Copyright National Portrait Gallery, London].	[18 Cent.]
4	Beckside, Kirkby Ireleth, aerial view, 1969. [Copyright *Barrow News and Mail*].	1969
5	Four Lane Ends, Kirkby Ireleth, aerial view, 1969. [Copyright *Barrow News and Mail*].	1969
6	Gill Beck Farm cruck roof with accompanying notes on cruck formations.	
7	Kirkby Hall chapel; interior roof and walls (2). [Copyright *Barrow News and Mail*].	
8	Kirkby Hall (4): exterior of house, interior and exterior view of room patterned stone. [Copyright *Barrow News and Mail*].	
9	Folio from a manuscript volume relating to the status of Kirkby church as a Peculiar of the Dean & Chapter of York.	[17 Cent.]
10	St. Cuthbert's Church, Kirkby Ireleth; tower and chancel views (2).	

RAIL CRASH – KIRKBY STATION – 1939

Thirty passengers were injured, three seriously, in the collision which took place at 1.45 am on the 25th August between two excursions returning from the Southport Flower Show. Inhabitants of Sandside still remember the impact, and the help they willingly gave the passengers, opening their houses, serving tea and comforting the injured.

KIRKBY RAIL CRASH 1939

KIRKBY RAIL CRASH 1939

120

11   Sandside, Kirkby Ireleth, aerial view.
[Copyright *Barrow News and Mail*].

12   Roa Island, near Barrow-in-Furness.
[Copyright *Barrow News and Mail*].

13   Cumbria and S. Scotland, aerial view.
[Copyright Avro Photographs, Manchester].

14   Crossing the Lancaster Sands; reproduction of painting.
[Copyright British Museum, London].

BD/F 11

11/1–42 The Kirby Family Photographs, 1963–1971.

42 items; almost all are small colour snapshots of the family, taken in America, *c.*1963–1971.

BD/F 12

12/1–9 Kirby Postcards.

Coloured postcards of American views; a few have correspondence on the back.

1   Adam Thoroughgood House 1636–1640 (6) showing Dining Room, side view, living room, rear view of house, and house exterior.

2   Appomattox Court House National Historical Park, Virginia (6): Clover Hill Tavern; the Parlour of the reconstructed McLean House; the Court House; reproduction of the surrender of General Lee to General Grant, 9 April 1865; New County Jail 1860–1870; painting of General Robert E. Lee leaving McLean house.

3   Cadets of Virginia Military Institute.

4   Natural Bridge, Virginia, once owned by Thomas Jefferson, ancestor of Anne Kirby.

5   Peaks of Otter Lodge and Lake, near Bedford, Virginia (6).

6   Pennsylvania Blue Stone.

7   The Shenandoah Valley from Blue Ridge Mountain.

8   Washington and Lee University, Lexington, Virginia (2) – facade of University building; the Lee Memorial Chapel.

9   Wyalusing Rocks, Pennsylvania.

BD/F 13

13/1–12 Postcards and Cards.

These items have been separated, presumably on the basis of their smaller size and local interest.

1   Bardsea Village in Winter, Cumbria.

2   Burlington School, Kirkby-in-Furness, 1877–1977.

3   Christmas card showing the Sir John Barrow Monument, Hoad Hill, Ulverston.

4   Christmas cards (5) from J.L. Kirby and family to Mr. and Mrs. Arthur Fieldhouse, and gift tags (6).

5   Christmas card: Edwardian style.

6   Furness Abbey, Cumbria: door of north transept.

7   Lanercost Priory, Cumbria.

8   Burneside, Cumbria.

9   Whitbarrow from High Foulshaw, Cumbria.

10   World map (17th century) by G. Blaeux 'Nova Totius Terrarum sive non orbis tabula'.

11   The Cathedral Church of The Holy and Undivided Trinity, Carlisle.

12   Brown's Hotel, Albemarle Street, 11 July 1967.

BD/F 14

14/1–19 Cards, Drawings, Maps and Plans.

A further miscellany of illustrative items in various sizes.

1   Maps of Essex (3): reproduction by Essex Record Office from John Norden's Manuscript 1594, from John Ogilby and William Morgan 1678; from John Chapman and Peter Andri 1777.   1594–1777

2   Facsimile of drawing showing area between Walney, Foulney Islands and mainland, sent to Samuel Pepys, Secretary of the Admiralty, October 1667 (from State Papers, Domestic Series, Charles 11 102–11).   1667

3	Poster advertising sale by auction of land at Soutergate, Kirkby Ireleth, by Alfred Coward, 16 March 1895.	1895
4	Plan of Kirkby Old Hall or Cross House: Upstairs and ground plan, taken from H. Swainson Cowper, 'The Homes of The Kirkbys of Kirkby Ireleth', *Transactions of the Cumberland and Westmorland Antiquarian and Archaeological Society*, O.S. (1895) XIII 269–86.	1895
5	Poster advertising sale by auction of freehold estate known as Bailiff Ground, Kirkby Ireleth, by Alfred Coward, 13 March 1896.	1896
6	Cartoon of football match at Kirkby, December 1907.	1907
7	Ordnance Survey maps: Lancashire sheets XI 5 and XI 9, 1913 edition with field names inked in by Ellen Fieldhouse.	1913
8	Sketches (2) in pencil and ink of St. Margaret's Church, Dalton-in- Furness, and of the Church of St. Mary of Furness, Barrow-in-Furness, copyright by Lilian Dixon, 1945–1946.	1945–1946
9	Cards mounted on hardboard showing the coats of arms of The Cavendish family, the Broughton family, the Kirkby family, the Preston family, the Lowther family, the Le Fleming family and the Urswick family, drawn by J.L. Kirby, 5 September 1966.	1966
10	Drawing of the Urswick Arms, drawn by J.L. Kirby, with accompanying memo., 12 September 1972.	1972
11	*Tourist's England* by Arthur Gaunt F.R.G.S.: original draft for poster advertising.	
12	Gillbeck Farm, Kirkby Ireleth: plan with field names and original tracing used to draw map.	
13	Hallstead Farm, Kirby Ireleth: plan with field names and original tracing used to draw map.	
14	Printed note paper for Lancashire Education Committee Rural Adult Education.	
15	St. Cuthbert's Church, Kirkby Ireleth: series of 7 watercolour drawings, with notes.	
16	Sketch in ink of an old photograph of Ghyll Beck, Kirkby Ireleth.	
17	Sketch in ink of St. Cuthbert's Church, Kirkby Ireleth.	
18	Sketch in ink of the Ship Inn, Kirkby Ireleth.	
19	Wreaks Bridge on the boundary of Kirkby Ireleth parish: oil painting by Dorothy C. Fieldhouse.	

BD/F 15

15/A–E Fieldhouse Tapes.

These tapes are stored separately; they particularly reflect Mrs. Fieldhouse's interest in country life and dialect.

Tape A *Side 1*

1–104	Sheep counting: 1–20 in Welsh by D.M. Richards.
105–208	'Auld Geordy and his Cow' narrated by Jane Wilson.
209–304	Baking Bread by Mabel Burns.
305–462	Cranberry picking by Jane Wilson.
463–476	Scones by Ellen Fieldhouse.
477–492	Potting Eggs by Mrs. Gray of Mavis Bank, Kirkby.
493–653	Cakes, soup and Roly Poly Pudding by Ethel Atkinson.
654–695	Ingredients for large rich 2 guinea cake by Mrs. W. Thompson.
696–714	The Laxton Plum Pudding, by Mrs. W. Thompson.
715–739	Elderberry Wine by W. Thompson.
740–765	Elderflower Wine and Sloe Gin by Joan Parsons of Kirk Beck House, Coniston.
766–799	Fruit Cake by Mrs. Franklin Moorhouse.
780–799	Barberry Ice Cream from *The Complete Confectioner* (1809) read by Arthur Fieldhouse.
800–906	Tom Proctor talks of farming in his youth.

Tape A *Side 2*

1–364	Tom Proctor talks about farming in his youth.
365–466	Folk Medicine collected by Joan Parsons – sprouts; nettles; water- cress; brimstone and treacle; cooked goose fat.
447–632	Folk medicine remedies supplied by A.W. Richards, 10 Hertford Street, Barrow-in-Furness:

- squills (for coughs)
- cold gas (whooping cough)
- raw beef (warts)
- dock leaf (nettle stings)
- stocking and salt (colic)
- stocking of left foot (sore throat)
- leach (bruises)
- butter (bumps)
- hot oatmeal and poultice (inflamation of lungs, pneumonia)
- nutmet or bee stings (rheumatism)
- oil (burns)
- hot bottle (boil)

     – bread poultice (abscess)
     – cobwebs (cuts)
     – ears pierced (weak eyes)
     – rum butter (babies at christening)
     – flour and cold earth (scabs).

633–723   Folk remedies supplied by Doris M. Hodgson, 6 Bristol Street, Walney.
     – water from boiled potatoes (chill blains)
     – soda, boric and zinc oxide (shingles)
     – stinging nettles (pleurisy)
     – elder blossom and papermint (chills and colds)
     – bran (anaemia)
     – lemon juice and boracic powder (hay fever)
     – cotton wool saturated with paraffin oil (lupus)
     – iron back covered with brown paper (lumbago).

724–631   Potato poultice for tonsilitis by Ethel Atkinson.

732–753   Miracle cure with a pea by Dr. Johnson of Dalton.

754–760   Oil of Juniper for kidney complaints and boiled vinegar for bruised limbs: remedies by Harry Holloway of Gill End.

761–773   Sugar on watercress for measles and yarrow tea made from flower heads for worms: remedies by Ethel Holloway.

774–970   Arthur Burns talks about his life as a Kirkby postman.

Tape B   Side 1
(Recordings 1–1171 made by Walter Dixon Knipe).

1–11   The Widow of Kirkby, story narrated.

12–66   Poor miners in Furness.

67–147   Cockles and Flakes.

148–204   Smuggling and wrecking in Furness.

205–232   T' Lebby Beck Dobby.

253–294   T' Invasion o' U'ston.

295–406   Amang T' Roundheads.

407–421   Story about pigs.

422–461   T' Siege o' Brou'ton.

462–557   The Terrible Knitters of Dent.

558–641   Dixon Lass and That Lad o' Thompson's.

642–925   Lakeland Smugglers, including Lanty Slee (whiskey distiller).

926–993   T' barring oot.

994–1080 Chapel Island.

1081–1171 Story about a holiday at Ravenstown in 1940.

1172–1532 Programme about dialect including interview with Ellen Fieldhouse, and Yvonne Adamson exploring Duddon-Grange 'Over Sands'.

Tape B   Side 2
Folk Medicine: A local history lecture by Dr. William Rollinson of Liverpool University.
1–497   Folk customs – marriages, deaths, funerals, school's barring out, Rowen tree magical properties.

Tape C   Side 1
1–10   The Widow of Kirkby.
11–64   Poor Miners in Furness.
65–140   Cockles and Fleeacks.
141–196   Smuggling and wrecking in Furness.
197–242   Lebby Beck Dobby.
243–281   T'Invasion o' U'ston.
282–388   Among t'Roundheads.
389–401   Story about pigs and farming at Satterthwaite.
402–439   Siege o' Brou'ton.
440–531   The Terrible Knitters of Dent.
532–608   Dixon Lass and That Lad o' Thompsons.
609–876   Lakeland Smugglers.
877–939   Baring Oot.
940–1019   Chapel Island.
1020–1102   Holiday at Ravenstown in 1940.
1103–1158   Programme about dialect including interview with Ellen Fieldhouse.
1159–1452   Yvonne Adamson explores Duddon-Grange 'Over Sands'.

Tape C   Side 2
1–72   Pace Egg Play presented by Ulverston Morris men at Broughton Beck.
73–139   Morris dances.
140–303   Slate Quarries in Kirkby-in-Furness 1966, by Bert Friar of Marshside.
304–515   Life in Kirkby in 1933, by Ellen Fieldhouse.
516–633   News about Kirkby over the years, by Ellen Fieldhouse.
634–679   Furness Dialect Phrases, by Walter Dixon Knipe.
680–739   Kirkby dialect, by Ellen Fieldhouse.
740–823   Jubilee of W.E.A. Council, Barrow-in-Furness branch: proposed speech by Ellen Fieldhouse 1969.
824–969   Lamplugh Club, by Rev. W. Braithwaite of Lanercost Vicarage.
870–1082   Barrow 1905–1918 by Ellen Fieldhouse, recorded 1972.
1083–1201   'Westmorland as it was', *Lonsdale Magazine*, 1822, narrated by Ellen Fieldhouse.

1202–1339 'Midnight Courtship', 'The Wedding Day', 'A Merry Meet', 'A Churn Supper', 'In the Churchyard' from Anderson's *Cumberland Ballads* (1805), narrated by Ellen Fieldhouse.

1340–1508 'Westmorland as it was', and 'The Stang' from the *Lonsdale Magazine* 1822, narrated by Ellen Fieldhouse.

1509–1537 'The Need Fire' from *A Commonplace Book* by T. Taylor of Sawrey, narrated by Ellen Fieldhouse.

Tape C   Side 3

1–20   Harper Gaythorpe: 'Church Bells in The Archdeaconry of Furness: Colton, Kirkby Ireleth, Broughton, Woodland and Seathwaite'. *Transactions of the Cumberland and Westmorland Antiquarian and Archaeological Society*, NS, (1902) 282–306 [283–95], narrated by Ellen Fieldhouse.

21–127   'Amang T'Rownheeads' from *The North Lonsdale Magazine and Furness Miscellany*, edited by Rev. Canon Ayre, (Ulverston 1898) III, no. 3.

128–148   John Trafford-Clay 'A Word with Jim Bobbin': poem.

149–162   'A Friendly Fitthers': poem.

163–171   Ingredients for Bible Cake, by Ellen Fieldhouse.

172–184   Petticoat Tails (cakes) by Ellen Fieldhouse.

185–329   'Merry Meet': radio programme made in Penrith featuring Cumbrian songs and comedy in Cumbrian dialect.

330–349   'Crossing the Sands,' *North Lonsdale Magazine* 1866, narrated by Phyllis Tyson.

350–386   'Bidding Funerals', by Ellen Fieldhouse.

387–398   'Customs at a Birth' and 'Folk lore: Rum Butter at Christenings', *North Lonsdale Magazine*, abridged by Ellen Fieldhouse.

399–412   Hand Fast marriages, and Illegal marriages, by Ellen Fieldhouse.

413–427   'The Widow of Kirkby', narrated by Margery Dickinson.

428–459   'The Wiving', *North Lonsdale Magazine* 1860, told by Jane Wilson.

460–468   Jane Wilson of Soutergate visits a new born child.

469–483   'A Novel Wager', 'Dalton Handicap 1879', song narrated by Arthur Fieldhouse.

484–658   November 1962. Dialect records by Tom Huddleston, Ravenscarr, farmer, used possibly for Band of Hope meetings: 'Adam and Mary'; 'Advice to Young Women'; 'Advice to Working Men'; 'Johnny and the Ghost'; 'Runaway Wedding'; 'Bite Bigger'.

659–723   'Siege o' Brou'ton' by Hugh Barton of Gill End.

724–825   Farming at Gill End, by Hugh Barton.
826–868   Dialect poem, narrated by Hugh Barton.
869–1000   Life in Kirkby, by Hugh Barton.
1001–1110 Much Urswick Tarn, *North Lonsdale Magazine*, 1866, narrated by Ellen Fieldhouse.
1111–1194 Local singing games.
1195–1276 History of the Rose Clan, by Ellen Fieldhouse.
1277–1319 Traditions to do with pennies, Shabby weddings and cock penny.
1320–1331 Joke about flocks.
1332–1386 Mummers; Pace Egging Play; Old Customs 'Barring Out' and 'May Gethling', by Ellen Fieldhouse.
1387–1441 Mumming article with quotations from actual play.
1442–1502 Old Christmas Time.

Tape C   *Side 4*
1–72   Pace Egg Play presented by Ulverston Morris Men at Broughton Beck.
73–137   Inaudible.
138–297   Slate Quarries in Kirkby-in-Furness 1966 by Bert Friar.
298–503   Life in Kirkby in 1933, by Ellen Fieldhouse.
504–617   News about Kirkby over the years, by Ellen Fieldhouse.
618–661   Furness dialect phrases, by Walter Dixon Knipe.
662–719   Kirkby dialect, by Ellen Fieldhouse.
720–801   Jubilee of W.E.A. Council, Barrow-in-Furness branch: proposed speech by Ellen Fieldhouse, 1969.
802–938   Inaudible.
939–1046   1905–1918, by Ellen Fieldhouse, recorded 1972.
1047–1538 Inaudible.

Tape D   *Side 1*
11–158   'Farm Service', narrated by Matthew Stables.
159–232   Poem by Matthew Stables.
233–363   Dialect conversation.
363–476   'Lakeland Words', by Ellen Fieldhouse.
477–559   'Pageant in Passion Week', *Lonsdale Magazine*, 1821.
560–584   Letter to the editor of the *Lonsdale Magazine* by J. Beck of Newton, July 1821.
585–620   Article about Kirkby Slate Quarries and surrounding area, narrated by Ellen Fieldhouse.
621–682   Jane Wilson talks about her childhood in Kirkby.
683–1042   Games 'Spell and Knur' written by "Blue Rock"; Cock fighting and old customs, narrated by Arthur Burns.

Old games and reminiscences of Barrow in the early 20th century, by Ellen Fieldhouse.
1043–1248 Richard Tyson talks about old Kirkby people.
1249–1389 'The Kirkby's', by Ellen Fieldhouse.
1390–1530 Mrs. Metcalfe: reminiscences on depression in 1930s.

Tape D *Side 2*
1–82 Mrs. Metcalfe, continued.
83–541 Recollections of Coniston and Ambleside by Mr. Knipe, born 1884.
542–770 Ellen Fieldhouse talks about local recipes and making of bread; rum butter; Grasmere ginger bread; oatmeal biscuit; the "old way" of making butter; beef and ham roll; sweet pie.
771–821 Ellen Fieldhouse talks about bottling fruit; Yorkshire Pudding.
822–940 Caramel toffee; seed cake; haverbread.
941–1204 The making of swills by Mr. Barker.
1205–1434 Furness dialect – explanation of specific words.
1435–1449 'Poor Relations' tale.
1450–1489 Sheep counting in dialect, by J. Wills.

Tape E *Side 1*
1–171 The Kirkby family by Ellen Fieldhouse.
172–290 Log book for Burlington School, Kirkby Ireleth beginning 1877 and including reminiscences of Ellen Fieldhouse's own teaching in Leeds.
291–320 Old documents of Kirkby Ireleth, by Ellen Fieldhouse.
321–389 Kirkby Ireleth Literary Society: speech given by Arthur Fieldhouse on the retirement of Dr. R. Parsons, President, 1953.
390–582 'Kirkby Night': Dialect recordings made by Dr. Harris of [1959] 'Farm Service' and a Dialect Conversation. Speakers – Richard Tyson, John Barr, and 'Dicky' Dickinson.
583–695 Singing games by four ladies, one gentleman from Kirkby and district.
696–839 'Chapel Island' narrated by Phyllis Tyson and Walter Dixon Knipe, using material by Edwin Waugh.
840–1066 Life as a postman in Kirkby, by Arthur Burns.
1067–1153 The baking of bread, by Mabel Burns.
1154–1350 Dinner from a Kail Pot . . . Baking a Cake, by Ethel Atkinson.
1351–1412 'The Widow of Kirkby', narrated by Margery Dickinson.

Tape E   *Side 2*

1–19   Dialect in Local Literature by Ellen Fieldhouse.
20–53   'Crossing the Sands', *North Lonsdale Magazine*, 1866, narrated by Phyllis Tyson.
54–145   'Seathwaite' and 'A Visit to Cockley Beck', by George Campbell.
146–184   Mrs. Humphrey Ward of Leven's Hall, Victorian novelist: extract from *Helbeck of Bannisdale*, narrated by Phyllis Tyson.
185–198   'Old Man sees a ghost', by Hugh Barton.
199–282   Local dialect, by Ellen Fieldhouse.
283–438   'Amang T' Rownheeads', by Freddy Wayles.
439–557   'T' Siege o' Brou'ton', by Hugh Barton.
558–986   Burlington Slate Quarries, by Bert Friar of Marshside.
987–1116 Sheep Counting by Joe Wills and D.M. Richards.
1117–1240 Lakeland words: story by Ellen Fieldhouse.
1241–1390 *Lonsdale Magazine*, 1821: extracts about the Pageant in Passion Week, and letter to the editor by J. Beck of Newton.
1391–1449 Kirkby Slate Quarries and surrounding area, by Ellen Fieldhouse.
1450–1540 Jane Wilson talks about her childhood in Kirkby, and the old mill.

BD/F 16

16/1–11 Tape Scripts

A single file of some of the scripts used in the tape recordings.

1   'Crossing the Sands' by Edwin Waugh, *North Lonsdale Magazine* (1866), [see Tape C].
2   'Customs at a Birth' and 'Folk Lore': Rum Butter at Christenings', *North Lonsdale Magazine* (1866) pp 22–26, [see Tape C].
3   Log Book for Burlington School, Kirkby Ireleth, beginning 1877, [see Tape E].
4   Reminiscences of Barrow, 1905–18, by Ellen Fieldhouse [see Tape C].
5   Life in Kirkby in 1933, [see Tape C].
6   'Lakeland Words': a tale of an outing by Ellen Fieldhouse; draft for the *Journal of the Lakeland Dialect Society*, no. 33 (1971) pp. 28–9, [see Tape D].

7   Bidding Funerals, [see Tape C].
8   Dialect in Local Literature, [Tape E].
9   The Kirkby family, [see Tape D and Tape E].
10   History of the Rose Clan, [Tape C].
11   News about Kirkby over the years, [see Tape C].

BD/F 17

17/1–7 Miscellaneous scripts

A file of further scripts not used in the tape recordings.

1   A Country Woman, 1933.
2   Draft introductory speech to 'Kirkby Night', 5 January
     1959.
3   Dialect Enquiry, July 1965.
4   Draft for article 'Dialect Enquiry in Furness', by Ellen
     Fieldhouse for the *Journal of the Lakeland Dialect
     Society*, no. 29, (1967).
5   Newcomers in Kirkby, 13 March 1969.
6   Draft for speech to Kirkby Literary Society, 3 January
     1972.
7   Draft notes for Ellen Fieldhouse's *Guide to the Parish
     Church of St. Cuthbert, Kirkby Ireleth*.
8   Ellen Fieldhouse's early memories: moving to Barrow;
     various relatives.
9   Ellen Fieldhouse: early life and growth of interest in
     dialect.
10   Ellen Fieldhouse: memories of W.E.A. movement.
11   Sundry rough lists of tape recordings (incomplete).

Miscellaneous artefacts.

A single large envelope with items forming a tailpiece to the collection.

- Cast iron pin.   *c.*1930
- Knur from the game Spell and Knur.
- Miniature rug teapot-stand made at Holker Street
  School, Barrow-in- Furness.
- Printed scarf with drawings of the Manx Greyhounds
  steamboats.
- Whistles chiselled from wood (2).

Appendix

A Fragment of Kirkby Ireleth Register, 1551.
Will of Richard Askew, 1551.
Will of William Kirkby, 1580.
Will of Henry Kirkby, 1582.
Will of Henry Kirkby, 1583.
Will of William Kirkby, 1587.
Inventory of Robert Kirkby, 1588.
Will of Robert Kirkby, 1588.
Inventory of Henry Kellett, 1615
Will of Roger Kirkby (proved 1618/19)
Will of John Kirkby, 1637/8.
Will of John Matson, 1657.
Will of William Woodburne, 1660.
Will of Ralph Kirkbie, 1665.
Will of Robert Matson, 1672.
Draft Agreement of customary tenants of Kirkby Ireleth in dispute with Colonel Kirkby, 1681.
Conveyance of William Woodburne, 1690.
Letter from William Kirkby to the Keeper of the Gaol at Lancaster, and the Constables at Kirkby Ireleth, 11 November 1692.
Will of William Kirkby of Ashslack, 26 January 1746.
A Particular of the Estate of Roger Kirkby.

EARLY MARRIED LIFE IN KIRKBY, 1933
(by ELLEN ROSE FIELDHOUSE)

At the end of our honeymoon week we bought a dog – a white rough haired terrier. When the Vicar called he said it was a wrong choice for a country dog. Since I was accustomed to the breed I didn't agree, but I soon did. Peter was the usual terrier but the cattle in the field disliked him while he went past them as if in shame. When he got away from his usual handling he chased sheep, persuaded two spaniels trained to the gun to do likewise and the only time I saw the circle at High Ghyll – the Kirk – was when I had to chase after Peter and drag him from the back of a sheep from where he was biting chunks of wool. He was a great fighter! Once he got going it was impossible to stop him. The fights always ended in the same way, with Peter underneath and people commiserating with me in case he should be killed. For once I held my peace, forebore to say he was then the victor, since the biting in that position was in accordance with his usual tactics. He was given to a school friend and did not return to Kirkby when we did. Mrs. Ethel Holloway who owned the spaniels, a real country lover, taught me many things and was also to become a life long friend. In those days we fell walked every afternoon ending in cups of tea either in Soutergate or Gill End. She it was, who said as we came down from the trips that Beckside was so clean that she felt like spitting on the doorsteps! Kirkby people as I have said were very kind to us and their homes were spotless and to use a north country expression 'one could eat from the floors'. Their children were well clad and well shod as was necessary when the lanes offered little shelter in bad weather. People used very little money. Only this afternoon a visitor told me of her grandmother who acted as a midwife. The only pay she had was 'in kind' – an occasional pat of butter along with the milk, a sack of potatoes, a sack of swedes, a basket of fruit or a few eggs were the usual rewards for help in times of sickness or help on the farm. There was a district nurse in Kirkby when we came, and I well remember her saying that people were so poor at one time that they often were only able to provide one candle for a confinement – the sole means of lighting. The people were forthright, their speech often in dialect, without frills, and they worked hard and lived frugally using as much of their own food as possible. The milk was fresh from the cow; butter was still made but not cheese. They grew their own vegetables and gathered sticks for firewood (elding). It was not easy to buy vegetables and considered improvident to buy firewood. Bought cakes, biscuits and chocolates were considered unnecessary luxuries and it was only during the Second World War when these things were apportioned out that folks started to

133

buy them. Bread was often put down in isinglass. Pickles – onions, piccalilly, chutney and red cabbage were made in the autumn. Much jam was made but not much bottling was done, although I remember doing some using mutton fat and bladder skin obtained from the butcher. We made blackberry jelly, strained in a bag, hanging from an upturned chair. Wine was made especially elderberry and cowslip. On most farms a pig was killed before Christmas and presents of pieces of pork, black puddings and sausages were distributed to friends. Some of the pork was salted and bacon and ham hung up on the rafters of the farm kitchen, ready for winter use.

Christmas cakes, Christmas puddings and mincemeat were usually made at home. Sweet mutton pies were still made and used by some people instead of the Christmas pudding. There was a tremendous amount of plucking – an art to which I never aspired – of chickens, hens, ducks, geese and turkeys. These were sold either in the village or in the Ulverston or Barrow markets. Presents of milk, cream and sausages were given to us by the suppliers at Christmas time. The largest shop in the village was and still is the Cooperative Store, founded by the quarrymen over a hundred years ago. Everyone belongs to it and one of our first outings in the honeymoon week was to join. The grocery department was excellent but with a country slant (preserving sugars, spices etc) and few luxuries. If one didn't go 'sticking' one asked for a box for firewood. Coal could be ordered and was delivered by the farmer engaged to do so when he could spare the time from his farm. The shop had a smell of many mixtures including the paraffin which was usually used for lighting. There was a Shoe Department selling strong shoes and clogs, and a drapery dept where excellent sock wool, red flannel and good woollen underwear were stocked. Nothing 'trashy' was ever kept. There was no demand for it. A traveller from the grocery dept and one from the drapery went round all the Kirkby hamlets for orders, but I can't remember how often they called although there was a weekly delivery of goods. It was and still is a very personal service and with goods sent out freely on approval.

Very few houses then had electricity but we were fortunate enough to have it, although many people deplored the fact that we had no house oven, only an electric cooker. It was frequently pointed out to us that no villager would live in our cottage since it had only a sitting room fire place, that the beck did get in and that my hunch about flooding was correct and since the floor had been lowered when the house was modernised this was an additional hazard. However, the beck had been cleared out and in the three years we lived in Soutergate we had no trouble and our precious books suffered no damage.

[from BD/F 16/5]

134

Easter 1933; the 'Jolly Boys.'

On the Good Friday in 1933 we heard a commotion in the village. It was a group of boys with blackened faces, dressed up in what looked like rags doing the traditional Easter Egging Play. This group came from Ireleth.

Later in the morning we climbed up to Friar's Ground, a charming ancient hamlet just under the fell, and the sound of the 'Jolly Boys' as they went the rounds of the village echoed from below. There we met Arthur Burns – the postman who did the high places. Our own postman was already an old friend shouting to my husband 'It's time to get up Arthur,' when he delivered our post at 7am. We stopped and talked to Arthur and he told us about the old mumming play. From Friar's Ground we climbed on to the fell and followed the fell wall and thence to Ulverston. In those days people walked to Ulverston Market on Thursdays regularly and it was quite usual to walk the five miles to the Whitsuntide and Martinmas fair. I well remember when the children from High Ghyll accompanied us as far as Ashlack as we came back. And how forlorn they looked in the distance as they set off for home via Pepper Wood and the Horse's Head while we followed the usual road to the summit of the fell that carried left for Gill End. Actually country children then walked miles and thought nothing of it.

[from BD/F 16/5]

135

FITCH'S

PATENT FIRE WHEELS

The only real effective Fire Lighter ever introduced to the public. One Wheel will light a fire without the aid of paper or wood; will boil three pints of water in a few minutes; will also cook a rasher of bacon, chops or steaks, and will give a bright flame for twenty minutes. They leave no mark on the grate; they are a strong disinfectant, and where constantly used will effect a great saving in other fuel. They are not liable to explosion.

DIRECTIONS FOR USE.

Place the Wheel at the bottom of the grate; then apply a lighted match, giving time for the Wheel to become thoroughly ignited; then place CINDERS loosely round and above.

MANUFACTURED ONLY BY

1870

HILL & CO.,

Caledonian Works, 8, Belle Isle, York Road, King's Cross, LONDON, N.

GRANT & CO., TURNMILL STREET, LONDON.

VICTORIAN ADVERTISEMENTS: Mrs. Fieldhouse made a large collection of these announcements, and filled one entire scrapbook. (BD/F 6/5).

136

FURTHER VICTORIAN ADVERTISEMENTS FROM MRS. FIELD-
HOUSE'S COLLECTION (BD/F 6/5).

The Jackdaw of Rheims

And a Nice Little Boy had a Nice Cake of Soap

Worthy of washing the Hands of the Pope.

1884

PEARS P

138

VICTORIAN ENGRAVINGS cut from magazines, form another large theme of Mrs. Fieldhouse's Scrapbooks; the literary tastes and attitudes which they portray form a strong contrast with modern times.

VICTORIAN ENGRAVINGS: a further example from BD/F 6/8.

CHAP. XV.

KIRKBY.

JAMES SHEPHERD, Eskawgate :
Cropped near ear, upper-halved far, two strokes down the near shoulder, and redded on the back of the head.

JAMES BUTCHER, Fellgate :
Ritted near ear, cropped far, a stroke over the back and down both sides.

MATTHEW NELSON, Hill :
Heathwaite Yeat Stock.—Cropped near ear, fold-bitted both sides far, a pop on the tail head,

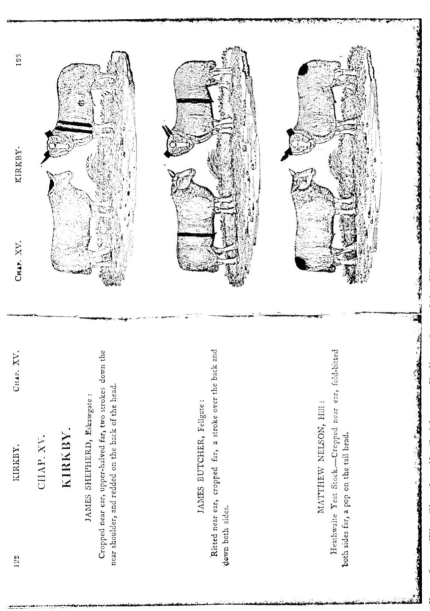

Page from 'The Shepherd's Guide or a Delineation of the Wool and Ear Marks on the Different Stocks of Sheep' published Penrith, c. 1820; an item in Mrs. Fieldhouse's collection of printed pamphlets. [BD/F 8/1].

10

THE "CRACKS" OF AN ORE-CARTER'S WIFE.

Cum sit thee ways doon, an' give us thee crack,
Aav been rayder badly and pain't a' me back ;
A crack does yan good, an' aav less to deah noo
Sen t' horses was selt, an' aav neah hay to poo.

Oor Jemmy sez t' horses hes dun us laal good,
Takkin o' in account it's no wunder they sud :
For they eat sek a heap o' good things, barn, aa lay
Thoo waddent beleev't if aa talkt for a day.

I't' dark winter mworniins, about three o'clock,
He shootit o't' lads ta git up, an' be gock !
He nivver cud lig a bit langer his sel,
For fear t' lads sud leave owt undun an' nit tell.

An' what cud aa deah when he was afeutt,
Bit up an' makt' poddish, while he went ta teutt
Amang t' horses an' git them ther crowdy an' meal ;
For hoo cud they work if they warrent fed weel?

Than away thay wad hurry to Cleator for ore,
Wi' sum hay in a sek an' ther best leg afore,
Thay com back o' sweat an' o' dust twice a day,
An' t' white horse as reed as if daub't wi' reed clay.

An' t' lads, to be shoor, sek seets they com heamm !
W' sek cleaz, an' sek feasses ! it was a fair sheamm !
An' than thay meadd t' blankets far warse nor git oot,
For thay leukt for o' t' warld like webs o' reed cloot.

11

Yan med wesh, barn, an' scrub till yan's fingers was sair,
An' nivver wad t' things o' yan's house be clean mair ;
T' varra hair o' yan's heed gat as reed as a fox,
An' it spoils o' my caps 'at's lockt up in a box.

Bit noo sen thayv oppent oot t' railway to t' Birks,
Weev partit wi t' horses an' cars, an' two stirks ;
Teahh lad's gitten liert, an' aav less ta dee,
An' tudder, nowt suits am but gangin to t' see

What changes it's mead in oor Hensigem street !
An' asteed o' reed muck we'll hev't clean as a peat ;
For weev Innderdale watter as cheap as oald rags,
An' we'el now see laal mair o' t' oald cars an' oald nags.

'Twas just tudder day 'at yan fell doon i't street,
'Twad ha' pittit thy heart, barn, ta leukk on an' see't,
Hoo it greannt as it laid till they reetit it up !
An' thay yokt it ageann and laid at it wi't' whup !

'Oor Jemmy, he sez, if he ivver gits poor,
Thay'll be settin am up for a mileston hees shoor,
Bit he laughs when he sez't, for he's summat laid bye,
An' he'll still mak a leevin as seaff as he'll try.

Beddelner-gill Feutt, April, 1856.

D.

Callander & Dixon, Printers, Market Place, Whitehaven.

Cumbrian dialect as represented in Mrs. Fieldhouse's collection of printed pamphlets: BD/F 8/2.

Spell + Knur:

Each player has 5 Knurs, and is allowed only one stroke at each Knur. The ground is pegged out in scores (20 yards), and a player's score is the total of completed scores of yards. Part scores do not count.

Meetings were called "Sweeps" in which any number of players took part. Any number of "Sweeps" could be played, and prizes were awarded for winners of each individual sweep.

A crack player could drive 10 or 11 score yards, and a good average for a crack player for 5 consecutive drives would be 40 score yards. Knurs must be made of wood, and were usually made from boxwood or lignum-vitae. Round in shape and roughly 1½" in diameter.

The club or striker is called a Pum.

P.T.O.

[from FIELDHOUSE SCRAPBOOK NO. 11 (BD/F 6/11)].

143

BOOK OF WORDS

TO BE SUNG BY THE

LEEDS HARMONIC UNION

AT THE

ENTERTAINMENTS

GIVEN BY

HIS GRACE THE DUKE OF DEVONSHIRE

TO THE

PARISHIONERS OF KIRKBY IRELETH

ON THE OCCASION OF THE

Public Opening of the Burlington Schools,

April 24th, 25th, and 26th, 1878.

SKIPTON:

EDMONDSON AND CO., STEAM PRINTERS, HIGH STREET.

[from BD/F 8/11].

THE BURLINGTON SCHOOLS

ENTERTAINMENT,

KIRKBY - IN - FURNESS.

THURSDAY, APRIL 25th, 1878.

Programme.

PART I.

GLEE............" Come, bounte   May "........ ....*Spofforth*
Leeds Harmonic Union.

SOPRANO SONG..." Bid me discourse "...*Sir H. R. Bishop*
Miss Winkworth.

PART SONG.........." Onward   ning "...............*Müller*
Leeds Harmonic Union.

TRIO.............. " My sweet Dorabella " ....*Mozart*
Messrs. Nunns, Stirk, and Ratcliffe.

PART SONG...... " When hands meet "...............*Pinsuti*

PART SONG...... "The Three Chafers "...............*Truhn*
Leeds Harmonic Union. The Bass Solo
by Mr. Turner.

DUET – (Soprano }
and Contralto)   } " When shall we meet "............*Glover*
Miss Winkworth and Miss Boothroyd.

PART SONG.. ...." The Sailor's Song "...............*Hatton*
Leeds Harmonic Union.

PART SONG..." When Evening's Twilight " ....*Hatton*
Leeds Harmonic Union.

OPERATIC SELECTION— " The Miserere Scene " ....
[(Il Trovatore)...*Verdi*

Interval and Addresses for 30 minutes.

PART II.

CHORUS..."Music sprea   y voice around" { (Solomon)...
{ *Handel*
Full Choir.

SOLO (Contralto) } "Thus rolling surges rise"... { (Solomon)
AND CHORUS   }   { *Handel*
Solo M   Boothroyd.

TRIO............ ." Lift th... eyes "...(Elijah)...*Mendelssohn*
Misses Winkworth, Willans, and Boothroyd.

CHORUS..."He watching over Israel"...(Elijah) *Mendelssohn*

QUARTETT..." Cast thy burden upon the Lord "...... ......
[(Elijah)...*Mendelssohn*
Miss Winkworth, and Messrs. Wright, Nunns,
and Turner.

SOLO (Soprano)..."But thou did'st not leave" { (Messiah) ...
{ *Mendelssohn*
Miss Winkworth.

CHORUS..." Lift up your heads "...(Messiah)...*Mendelssohn*

CHORUS......... " Hallelujah "......(Messiah)...*Mendelssohn*

FINALE—NATIONAL ANTHEM..."God Save the Queen"

Edmondson and Co., Printers by Steam Power, Skipton.

[from BD/F 8/11].

145

BURLINGTON SCHOOL CLASS, *c*. 1900. The Headmaster, Mr. E.N. Lewis, (1853–1913) was also Organist and Choirmaster at the Parish Church.
[from BD/F 6/11].

Kirkby Quarries – 'going up the Incline'. The tramway to the main line dropped down 800 feet, and worked by gravity. It lasted 100 years before being replaced by a road system in 1952.

ST. CUTHBERT, KIRKBY IRELETH

PARISH MAGAZINE

VICAR:

Rev. W. HARRY ROBERTS, M.A., Hon. C.F.

Churchwardens:

Mr. G. Trenwith, J.P., Mr. H. Briggs, Mr. J. Cartmel, Mr. W. Moorhouse.

Secretary of Church Council : Mr. M. Stables.
Organist & Choirmaster : Mr. Francis W. Raby.
Verger : Mr. R. H. Shepherd.
Sexton : Mr. A. F. Deason.

Services:

SUNDAYS: HOLY COMMUNION, 8 a.m., also 1st and 3rd Sundays in the month after Morning Prayer.   SAINTS' DAYS, as announced in Church.
MORNING PRAYER, 10-30.   EVENING PRAYER, 6 p.m.
Children's Service, 1st SUNDAY, 2-15 p.m.
Sunday School, in Beckside School, 9-45 a.m. and 2 p.m.
Mothers' Union, Girls' Friendly Society, and other meetings as announced.

From the incomplete series of church maragizes in BD/F 9/67.

147

Newfield Hotel, Seathwaite after navvy 'riot', 1904.
POSTCARDS FROM BD/F 6/11.

Village cricket team, 14 July 1913.

Band of Hope – 'this was an annual event'.
ILLUSTRATIONS FROM BD/F 6/11.

'The Drama Class' – presented at Kirkby 1954.

The Punch Bowl Inn was the headquarters of the Kirkby Friendly Society, registered in 1848, which provided simple insurance against sickness and bereavement. A few relics from the Society survive in the collection.

This was part of the original portion of the Furness Railway line, opened in 1846.
POSTCARDS FROM BD/F 6/11.

The Mill: once an important centre of agricultural life, but now converted into a dwelling house. The mill is mentioned as being in use during the 16th Century.
ILLUSTRATIONS FROM BD/F 6/11.

Kirkby Hall entrance drive, c. 1900. The boys are Matthew Bolton, Charlie Harrison and Robert Smith.

The Hall was the main dwelling house of the Kirkby family for much of their time as Lords of the Manor, which ended early in the 18C.

From a True Friend at KIRKBY

POSTCARDS FROM BD/F 6/11.

152

Post Office and Hotel.

Hugh Jones, manager with slate workers from Kirkby Quarries, *c.* 1900.

An early view of members of the Church of Christ at Wallend, erected in 1876.
ILLUSTRATIONS FROM BD/F 6/11.

The Co-op Fire: The Dalton Fire Brigade was called to the Society's premises on
16 March 1905, when damage amounting to £400 was done to the property and
stock.

KIRKBY WOMEN'S INSTITUTE: YEAR? (From BD/F 6/11).

155

Customs at a Birth.

Rum butter was made before, the birth as it was thought that a lying in woman would never recover unless she had plenty of rum butter. The butter was first melted (not boiled) in a brass pan till the milk ran to the top, and the salt sank to the bottom. The floating ingredients were then skimmed off, and the butter poured off clear from salt and sediment. A quantity of rum and sugar having been well beaten together in a bowl with a little grated nutmeg, was then mixed with the butter, and carefully stirred until it was beginning to set.

The "wives" who had promised to help at the birth were "laited", and as soon as they arrived they helped in any way they could. When the child was born the head was washed all over with rum, and the men drank the health of the baby in something stronger than tea. Before the women departed at whatever time of day or night it might be they sat down to a good tea.

As soon as the mother was well enough she invited all her female friends to a second teaparty called the "wiving" when they attended with presents - bread, butter sugar and wine. They sat down to a good tea - the rum butter often appearing in a large old fashioned valuable china bowl which had been in the family for generations.

The "Christening" itself was a more formal affair. All friends and relations as well as the sponsers were invited and often the clergyman and the clerk joined in. The evening was spent in merrymaking and drinking.

[from BD/F 16/2].

156

Bidding funerals.

Upon the death of anyone in the district it was the regular ancient custom to invite acquaintances as well as the friends and relations to attend the funeral. This was called the bidding. In thinly populated areas it was usual to bid two from each homestead, but in more populous areas only one was bidden at each house.

When the guests arrived at the house of mourning on the appointed day, they found a large table set out, covered with cheese, wheat bread and oat cake and ale, cold or warm, according to the season. A long time was allowed for refreshment before the removal of the corpse took place. Each person was expected to view and touch the body. This arose from an old superstition firmly believed, that if the murderer touched the person he had murdered, the corpse would begin to bleed. All who attended funerals were expected to pass this ordeal.

A small loaf or cake — the aval bread was given to each and he or she was expected to carry this home and eat it with the rest of the family in religious remembrance of their departed neighbours.

It was customary in some localities for singers to head the funeral procession chanting hymns or psalms along the route. Sometimes when the church was a long way off the solemn tunes were taken up at intervals, and the sands of the voices fell plaintively, on the ear as the sorrowful train wended its way along the country lanes or by the fell side to the last resting place.

Mr Whitaker, Vicar of Seathwaite says that as a boy when his father was Vicar of Ulpha he was told of this custom by an old woman in the parish.

An old lady's will of 1704 bequeaths "twenty shillings to be distributed by my said son — in flaw to such young men" and others who shall sing psalms before my corpse to ye Church all ye time of my funeral".

In some parts of Low Furness where the Parish Church was at a considerable distance, the bearers who carried the corpse on a rude kind of bier were obliged to rest at intervals along the road and places were erected by the road side, here and there called resting trees upon which the coffin was placed until a relay was provided and all had rested.

In these districts it was common to distribute the oval bread before starting and each person received a cake and a quarter. At the resting quarter stone each bearer ate the cake to refresh themselves and keep up an ancient custom.

Before 1547 when the Broughton churchyard was consecrated all the dead from Seathwaite, Dunnerdale, Woodland and Broughton were brought to the Mother Chapel of Kirkby Ireleth to be buried.

"Wonderful Walker" of Seathwaite used to give the following tradition for the erection of his chapel. "The inhabitants were conveying a body to Kirkby for interment in the depth of winter when the snow began to fall. By the time they had reached a part of the hill above Newfield Farmhouse, they could go no further with the body and it was left on the common for a few days. After this they sent a petition to the Earl of Derby (lord of the manor) stating the above case, praying he would erect them a place of worship, as they were a poor class of people unable to do so themselves."

About a hundred years ago Mr Sawrey of Broughton Tower said that he had written to show that the Earl of Derby did build this chapel.

In former times, before there was either a church or burial ground in Coniston, the dead were regularly conveyed on sledges to Ulverston Church for interment. One one occasion it happened that the corpse of a person named Jenkins, from the neighbourhood of Tiberthwaite, was thus travelling on one of these ancient hearses to his long home.

It happened, however, that in crossing a small brook a quarter of a mile from the place where Coniston Church now stands, that the coffinless body slipped from the sledge. It was some time before the disconsolate widow, and the other mourners, observed the absence of the principal personage; he was however found in the stream, and without any further attempt to escape,

was safely conducted to Ulverston. Hence the brook bears the name of Jenkin-sike to this day.

The passing bell so named from being originally tolled when anyone was passing from life, so that those who heard it might pray for the person dying was tolled at intervals on the day of death and on the occasion of the funeral.

All passengers, whether riding, driving or walking on meeting, or coming up with a funeral procession would stop until the mournful cortège had passed on, at the same time uncovering the head out of respect to the awful presence of death, even if they had been unacquainted with the deceased during life.

Index of Names

163

Robert, 20
Tamer, 20
William, 4, 29
Lanty Slee, 91
Laury, John, 23
Le Fleming, see Fleming
  family, 121
Lesh, Edward, 19
  Sarah, 19
  William, 19
Lindow, Ann[e], 28
  James, 22, 28(2)
  Mary, 28
  Phebe, 28
  Thomas, 28
  William, 28
Lisseter, E.M., 81
Livesey, Hannah, 105
  J., 58
Lombardo, Loretta, L., 47
Long, J.A., 73
  John, 25
Lowther, family, 123
  John, 34

McAtee, W.A., 67
MacDougall, William, 57
McKeo, John, 21
McKnight, see Knight
Maddoc, John, 19
Madocsword, John, 19
Margaret, Princess, see Snowdon, Coun-
  tess of
Marr, Robert, 70
Marshall, Dr. J.D., 67, 108
Martin, James, 50
  M.G. de Renzy-, 80
Mason, see Mayson, Miss, 75–76
  Clyde, W., 9
  George, 59
  H., 63
  Rebecca Alice, 59
Massicks, Mary, 27
Matheson, Rev., 58
Matron, Frances, 27
Matson, An [Anne], 16
  Elizabeth, 14
  Francis, 6

John [Jo'], 8, 15
Margret, 15
Robert, 16
Roger, 14
Thomas, 16
William, 15
Mayson, John, 18, 26, 37
  Thomas, 26
Melville, James, 9(2), 49, 86, 100, 102,
  105–106, 108, 110, 115
Metcalf, Mrs., 129
Michaelson, Robert, 26
  Thomas, 26
Middleton, Jane, 22
  William, 20
Miller, Agnes, 31
Millner, Joseph, 25
Miniken, Bridget, 32
  Elmer, 32
  John, 32
  Margaret, 32
  William, 32
Moore, John B., 110
Moorhouse, Franklin, 124
  Jessie, 75
Moses [Mozes], E., 104
  John, 12
Moss, John, 21
Mulgrave, Lord, 29
Muncaster, A., 85
Murray, Beatrice, 83
  Robert, 97
Myers, William, 59

Nealson, see Nelson
Nelson [Nealson], Anne, 36
  Hannah, 58
  Henry, 17, 29, 32–33
  James, 16
  John, 29, 32–33
  Margaret [Margret], 23, 29
  Robert, 31
  Samuel, 18, 32–33, 35
  Thomas, 18, 22–27, 29–32, 36
Newby [Nuby], Agnes, 22
  Ella, 76
  James, 24

169

Index of Places

173

174

Moss House, 4
  Pear Tree, 4
  Prospect, 4
  Rectory, 4
  Skill Hill, 77
  Wallend, 4
festivals
  coronation festivities, 62, 64
  Jubilee celebrations, 60
  Marshside festival, 63
Gillbecke, Gillbeck, Ghyll Beck, *see* Gill
  Beck
Gill Beck, 2, 4–5, 10–11, 16–17(2),
  26–27, 42–43, 123
Gill End, 75, 125, 127
Head Cragg, 111
High Ghyll, 3
houses
  Avondale, 85
  Bankhouse, 26
  Gill House Beck, 63
  Glen Cragg, 62–63, 77
  Greenhow, 64
  High Bank, 4
  High Ghyll, 4, 63
  Laurels, 83
  Little Croft, 63, 69, 76
  Low House, 15
  Moor View, 9
  Prospect Cottage, 75
  Prospect House, 64
  Seattle, 68
  Soutergate House, 49, 61, 63
  Stone Arthur, 44
  Toad Hole, 23
inns, 3
  Punch Bowl, 61
  Ship, 84
Kellet Ground, 19, 48
Kirkby Hall, 3–4, 63, 84, 118
  chapel, 66, 69, 118
  cross, 5
  Kirkby Hall Farm, *see* farms
  sale at, 45
  structure of, 5, 123
Mearbeck, Merbecke, Merrebeicke,
  Mier Beck, *see* Merebeck
Merebeck, 14, 17, 19, 21, 32, 41, 44

mills, 31, 65–66, 71, 128, 130
  Beckside, 35
  Grizebeck, 35
police station, 9
post office, 64
  postman, 125, 129
railway station, 3, 61, 69, 108, 118
  train crash at, 3, 8, 108, 118
Sandside, 15, 18, 21, 24–25, 29, 33, 35,
  49, 58(2), 62, 76–77, 121
  gospel hall, 70
  manor court at, 31
shows
  art, 66
  flower, 70, 106
  Kirkby, 65, 83
societies
  Beckside Supper Club, 82
  British Legion, 67–68, 86
  Co-operative Society, 1, 10, 114
    fire at, 63
    jubilee, 62
  Cricket Club, 63(2)
  Drama Group, 2, 63–65, 67
  Football Club, 85
  Kirkby and Broughton Choral Group,
    62
  Kirkby and District Floral and Horti-
    cultural Society, 62(2), 65, 68,
    83–86, 116
  Kirkby and Grizedale Old People's
    Welfare Committee, 69, 85
  Ladies' Guild, 82
  Literary Society, 1, 46, 65(2), 67–68,
    82, 86, 103, 110, 129, 131
  Mothers' Union, 68–69, 84–86, 102, 104
  Over 60's Club, 67, 68–70, 82–86,
    101–105
  Scouts, 83, 84, 103
  Women's Institute, 66, 70, 82–86,
    102–106
  Women's Unionist Association, 69
Soutergate, 6, 13, 18, 20, 22, 24, 27, 32,
  34, 40, 43, 44, 59, 62, 75–77, 83,
  123, 127
Marsh Book, 33
  owners of, 45
Soutergate House, 49, 61, 63

175

Index of Subjects

Hermits, 86

Inns, 3
  Broughton, King's Head, 87
  Dalton, Black Dog, 87
  Hawkshead, Drunken Duck, 73
  Kirkby-in-Furness, Punch Bowl, 61
  Ship, 84
  Lowick, Farmer's Arms, 71
  Walney Island, New Inn, 102

Magazines and Journals
  Cassell's Family Magazine, 49, 51, 61,
    111
  Cassell's Popular Educator, 111
  *Cumberland and Westmorland Antiqua-
    rian and Archaeological Society Jour-
    nal*, 6, 12, 45, 49, 93, 112–116, 123,
    127
  Cumbria, 77, 79, 100
  Lakeland Dialect Society Journal, 79–81,
    90–92, 130
  London Society Illustrated Magazine, 56,
    61
  North Lonsdale Magazine, 3, 6–7, 45, 71,
    90, 126–130
  South Carolina Historical Magazine, 47
  Vickers News, 86, 88, 96–105, 107,
    116(3)
  V.S.G. Link, 116(2)
  Woman at Home, 61
  Yorkshire Dialect Society Journal, 79,
    92–93
Mills, *see* Index of Places under particular
  places
Mines, 81, 125
  Coniston, 103
  Duddon, 103
  Hodbarrow, 95
  Newton, 88
  Roanhead, 97
  Stainton, 88, 97
  Urswick, 104
  Yarlside, 89

North Lonsdale
  Field Club, 7
  Rural District Council, 65
  Society, 10, 88, 97, 101, 103, 106

Operatic and Dramatic Societies
  Furness Drama Association, 98
  Kirkby Ireleth Drama Group, 2, 63–65,
    67
  Ulverston Amateur Operatic Society, 74

Parish Registers, *see* Index of Places under
  particular places
  Lancashire Parish Record Society, 70

Quakers
  Kirkby meeting house, 57
  Swarthmoor meeting house, 57

Recipes, 74–79, 85, 108, 124, 129(2)

Schools, *see also* Index of Places under
  particular places, 66–67, 110
Ships, 73–74, 106–07, 109
  manx boats, 18
Shows, *see* Index of Places under particular
  places
Swillmakers, 67, 102, 129

Taxes, 2, 6
  Land Tax Assessment, 42
  Land Tax Bill, 21, 33, 39
  Land Tax Return Form, 40
  Slate Tax, 39–40
Tithes
  Award Book, 48
  Lamplugh, 4
  Redemption Communion, 67
  Tithe Barn, 64

Vickers Ltd., 88, 96–99, 101, 104,
  106–109, 114, 116
Vickers News, 86, 88, 96(2), 98, 99,
  100–105, 107, 116(3)
Vickerstown, 97